ROLLS-ROYCE HER

CW01020811

THE MERLIN
IN PERSPECTIVE
- the combat years

Alec Harvey-Bailey

HISTORICAL SERIES No 2

Published in 1983 by the
Rolls-Royce Heritage Trust
PO Box 31 Derby England

Fourth edition 1995

©1981 A H Harvey-Bailey

This book, or any part thereof,
must not be reproduced in any form without the
written permission of the Publisher.

ISBN 1 872922 06 6

Cover picture of Merlin-powered Spitfire I's of
65 Squadron flying from Hornchurch.

Reprinted with minor amendments in 2003 by
Océ Document Services, Bristol.

CONTENTS

FOREWORD

Alec Harvey-Bailey served with Rolls-Royce for over forty years and his associations with the company began long before he joined its employ. His father was a senior executive of Rolls-Royce for the majority of his working life. In consequence Alec's personal memories span an era encompassing recollections of meeting Sir Henry Royce, the Schneider Trophy Seaplane contest and the epic days of motor car development in the 1920s and 1930s before he actually joined the company shortly before the Second World War.

Following a brief period of association with motor cars, after the start of the War Alec joined defect investigation and was soon given charge of the task on both the Merlin and Griffon aero engines. The task involved not only the examination of damaged service engines and being a party to the development of solutions to engineering problems but also the definition of technically effective repair techniques. Furthermore his work was far from confined to the workshop for he spent a great deal of his time, including many weekends, with the Squadrons, finding out for himself. He flew in service aircraft when necessary and became familiar at first hand with the many aircraft types powered by the Merlin in particular.

The pressures placed on Rolls-Royce by the need to keep one jump ahead of a determined adversary, and the gaunt nature of life in those war years made an indelible impression on Alec. These factors, together with his prodigious memory, make him unique in his understanding of the Merlin engine and its contribution to this crucial period of aviation history.

Over the years, particularly during the course of his overseas assignments, Alec and his wife Joan, who was an able unpaid personal assistant through many crises, often entertained colleagues from the factory. The topic of conversation on such occasions was almost always Rolls-Royce and, as evenings wore on, conversation tended to hark back to earlier years. The clarity of Alec's memories was such that on more than one occasion colleagues suggested that he should write it all down. Their words did not go unheeded, and pondering on them Alec recalled that his father had tried to do this. But he had left it too late.

It was this fact in particular that steeled Alec's determination to set down his memories before they became blurred either by the passage of time or the effects of advancing years. More than a decade ago he therefore started dictating his memories of the Merlin during odd moments of spare time in Beirut and Cairo. As the story came together he began to refine its contents by repeated dictation of its various elements until the equilibrium he sought was achieved in the narrative.

Since returning to Britain further work has gone into the text of this book. Indeed, to achieve the accuracy of narrative essential to satisfy his principles, Alec has put more hours and more sweat into his story than he could ever be persuaded to admit. Furthermore he has been able to cross-check his facts, not only with those of his colleagues who remain, but also with friends he made in the services at the time. Many have had distinguished careers – some in the Royal Air Force and others, since the war, in the aviation industry.

The outcome of Alec's effort is contained in this volume. Despite the problems, none of which have been overlooked in these pages, the Merlin emerges as a giant of aero engine history. No other aero engine of the Second World War has, as far as I know, ever been written up in such a thorough manner. Neither can I think of one that is more deserving of such a treatise. To the allied cause it made an unrivalled contribution and for Rolls-Royce it was instrumental in causing a metamorphosis. Rolls-Royce entered the war years as a small high-quality manufacturer in a Derby side road. It emerged as a major British company, the magic of whose name is now admired throughout the World.

For the best part of a decade now I have been privileged to be able to help Alec in a small way with the preparation of this volume. I hope you will share with me in the thought that this record of the Merlin had to be published, and the belief that it does full justice to a great aero engine.

M H Evans
Chairman, Rolls-Royce Heritage Trust

ACKNOWLEDGEMENTS

My task has entailed accurate cross checks and I am grateful for confirmation and advice so freely given. On operational and flying matters I should like to thank Air Marshal Sir Dennis Crowley-Milling, KCB, CBE, DSO, DFC, Air Marshal Sir Ivor Broom, KCB, CBE, DSO, DFC, AFC, Group Captain John Cunningham, CBE, DSO, DFC, Captain H C Rogers, OBE, DFC, Mr A J Heyworth, DFC, Mr H N D Bailey, and Mr A G McIntyre, AFC. For advice on contemporary Allied and Enemy equipment, Mr Humphrey Wynn of the Air Historical Branch (RAF), MoD, has been extremely helpful. For technical cross references my thanks go to Mr A C Rudd, Mr J R Nutter, Mr R Forrester, and Mr D Birch. In the interests of accuracy the graphs and performance curves used have been taken from data prepared by Cyril Lovesey CBE. My thanks go to Miss B S Jackson for typing assistance and to members of the Rolls-Royce Heritage Trust Derby Branch for their co-operation and hard work to make this publication possible.

Alec Harvey-Bailey
July 1983

PERSONNEL REFERENCE SYSTEM

Use is made in the text of the personnel reference system, instituted by Royce and still used in the Company today. In this system, all Company personnel are addressed by a 'reference' which enables internal communication to be carried out without the encumbrance of formal rank and title. Examples used in this text are,

Ald	Freddie Allwood
By	R W Harvey-Bailey
Dor	Ray Dorey
EJW	Whitehead
Hs	E W Hives
Lov	Cyril Lovesey
Mx	John Maddocks
Rm	W A Robotham

AUTHOR'S NOTE

The fourth edition of 'THE MERLIN IN PERSPECTIVE – the combat years' contains additional information of historical interest in Appendices V through VIII.

Alec Harvey-Bailey
March 1995

The Merlin in Perspective
The Combat Years

Introduction

This small booklet attempts to look overall at the wartime Merlin, to examine the pressures on its development and the task set manufacturing and support facilities, but above all at its role as the major combat engine in the one big air force which saw the War through from September 1939 until August 1945. Its history and achievements were crowded into a short span of years, which is remarkable because no other engine type has approached the production run in numbers or operational scope.

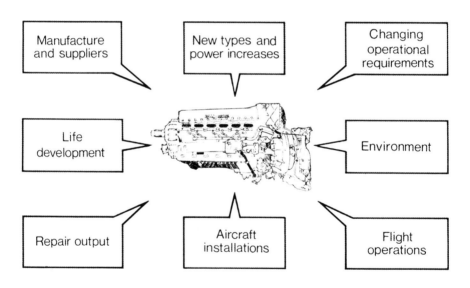

1 Merlin – the perspective

The Merlin was instrumental in converting Rolls-Royce from what has been described as a brilliant sprat in the ocean of technology into a world contender in aero engine manufacture. Its serious design did not start until 1933. Its once familiar exhaust note started as an infant cry in the sky in 1935, became the sound of the RAF in the Battle of Britain, grew to a crescendo in 1945 and then died away to become, when heard in a lone Hurricane or Spitfire, as nostalgic as the rumble of a Le Mans Bentley or the scream of an ERA.

Early background

To look back a little, although Rolls-Royce had developed an enviable reputation in the aero engine field by 1918 and had subsequently powered the great pioneering flights, including the start of civil aviation, the 1920s saw the Company slip into third place behind Bristol and Napier. At the end of the twenties it was the performance of the R type racing engine which overshadowed the competition, both British and foreign, in the Schneider Trophy races and put Rolls-Royce into serious contention for major RAF contracts. Both Royce and Hives, who was the head of the Experimental, saw the need for a fighter engine that would, in suitable aircraft, provide Britain with high quality air defence. This was the PV12. In an attempt to provide greater robustness at low weight, it departed from Rolls-Royce practice in having cylinder blocks and crankcase as a unit with detachable heads. It also had a new reduction gear with double helical teeth. The engine ran in this configuration but the one-piece block and crankcase was deemed unacceptable in terms of maintainability and the helical gear gave trouble. A redesign was carried out by Elliot, then Chief Engineer, reverting to detachable cylinder blocks and a spur reduction gear. A more definitive engine appeared retaining the 5.4 in bore and 6 in stroke, 1,650 cubic in (27 litre) capacity. It thus lay between the Kestrel and the R with the object of achieving 1,000 hp as a normal combat power, but with scope for further development while maintaining minimum frontal area.

Unhappily, for war clouds were gathering, a major departure in cylinder design had been made, adopting as the result of single cylinder tests a ramp of semi-penthouse combustion chamber [2]. In main engine tests it did not give the anticipated performance and suffered from cracking in manufacture and service, probably due to its lack of symmetry. Thus, having designed a two-piece block to eliminate the internal coolant leaks to which the Kestrel type of one-piece block was subject, the Merlin continued the hazard in a more serious form. Initial production had been committed and one can almost hear Hives saying in his quiet way 'We had better get back to the problem we know about'.

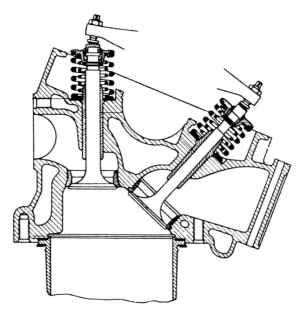

2 Merlin I ramp head cross section

  He made the courageous decision to revert to a one-piece block with a single plane combustion chamber for immediate production [**3, 4**] and to start the design of the two-piece block which enabled the Merlin to achieve major power increases with a reliable cylinder assembly.

Such were the development efforts that a production standard single piece block Merlin II, installed in a Hawker Horsley, flying from Hucknall, completed 100 flight hours in 6½ days in the summer of 1937 [**35**].

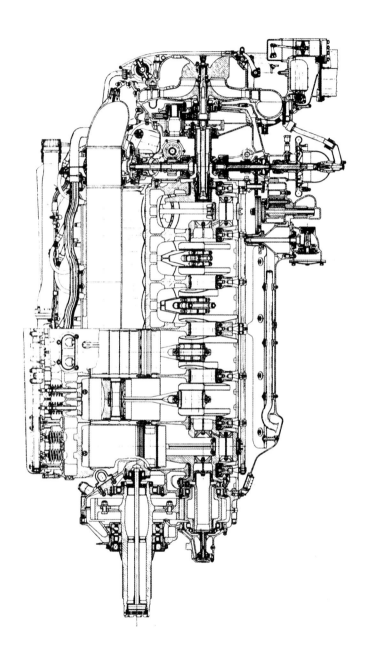

3 Merlin II longitudinal cross section

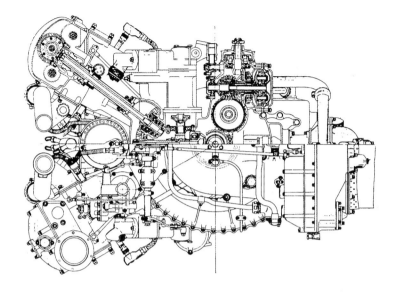

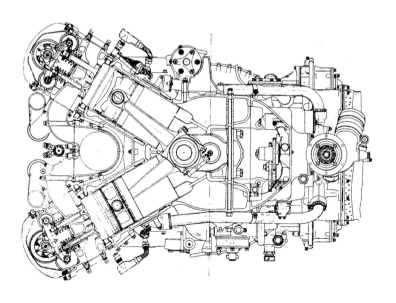

4 Merlin II transverse sections

Expansion

While this was going on the Air Ministry had launched the shadow factory programme based on Bristol engines who were then the major supplier to the RAF. Rolls-Royce expansion was being met by the building and staffing of the Crewe factory, leased from His Majesty's Government, and which contributed to engine supply in the Battle of Britain. At Glasgow an Air Ministry factory was under construction, to be managed by Rolls-Royce, and the Ford Motor Company was given the task of setting up another major factory at Manchester. As the War went on the Packard Motor Company of Detroit undertook the manufacture of the Merlin in the United States.

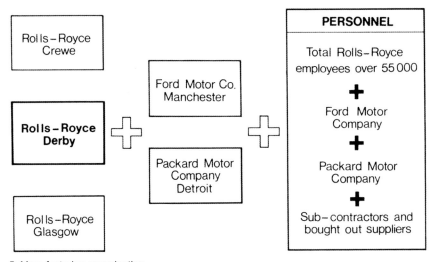

5 Manufacturing organisation

To handle the massive repair arisings, the Derby repair organisation was expanded and moved to various locations in Nottingham, using the lace mills and in particular Radford Mill in Garden Street, a triumph of improvisation by Len Archer who had been in charge of Chassis Test. Glasgow set up a facility which also handled Packard Merlins. Sunbeam Talbot, Alvis and de Havilland were also brought in, and the RAF started 32 Maintenance Unit at St Athan. The RAF also had its own bases throughout the Middle East, North Africa and Far East. These included such famous locations as the Toura Caves near Cairo [36] with all sorts of subcontracting in the back streets of that amazing city [37], Maison Blanche at Algiers, Drigh Road at Karachi and Bangalore in south India. The Royal Navy had its own Repair Yards, including Fleetlands, which handled Merlins.

Excluding the overseas bases and the Royal Navy, 50,000 repair engines were produced during the War.

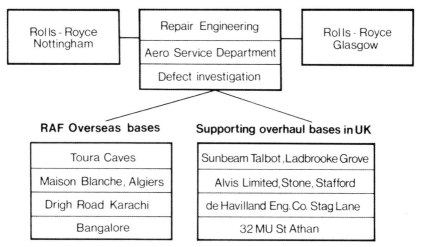

6 Repair and support organisation

When the first Merlin I was built Rolls-Royce employed less than 7,000 people, on both aero engines and chassis. Besides the Merlin, Peregrine, Vulture, Griffon, EXE, and Pennine, a petrol injection two stroke and a marine Merlin were under design and development; a wide span for such a small team. In 1938 Dr Griffith joined the company to start work on gas turbines.

By the end of the War in Europe the Company employed over 55,000 people plus a host of suppliers and subcontractors. It also provided technical expertise in a generous and unstinted flow to Ford and Packard. Senior technical staff including James Ellor Snr and Colonel Barrington were loaned to Packard. Ford and Packard employees are not included in the total above.

As there had only been a trickle of other production engine types and as the gas turbine business did not get going until 1943, nearly all this expansion can be attributed to the Merlin. After the War when the dust of contraction had settled the level of employees did not fall below 30,000.

Wartime output of new Merlins was more than 160,000 of which over 100,000 were built in Britain. The Merlin came to the forefront in the air fighting during the Dunkirk period and subsequently in the Battle of Britain where it was almost synonymous with Hurricane and Spitfire. The engines which carried the brunt of the fighting were basic single speed supercharged types, notably the Mark II and III although some Merlin XIIs in Spitfire IIs with higher geared superchargers and a few Merlin XXs with two speed superchargers in Hurricane IIs saw service in the Battle. 100 octane fuel was available enabling 12 lb boost to be used, giving more power at lower altitudes on earlier types and being essential for the more powerful engine types coming into service.

The important issue in the Battle was the supply of new and repaired engines. It is a fact that at the start of July 1940 the RAF had over 600 Merlin powered fighters on the squadrons, serviceable and available for operations. By the end of September, this number had increased to over 700.

Developments

The range of engines built during the War included single-stage single-speed superchargers, single-stage two-speed superchargers and two-stage two-speed superchargers with intercooling. Most engines had electric starters but a limited number had Coffman cartridge starting.

There was a major redesign of the two-stage two-speed engine to embody single point fuel injection, end to end crankshaft lubrication, and a supercharger with an overhung first stage impeller (Merlin 100 series). The 130 series was a cleaned up or Schneiderised version for the de Havilland Hornet, with downdraught induction, Corliss throttle, side mounted coolant pump and handed propeller rotation. Although engines were built during the War the aircraft did not see Wartime squadron service.

There was a development of the single stage engine for York [38] and Lancastrian [39] aircraft in the transport role which gave a start to post War commercial operation. This led to a civil two stage engine which powered the Avro Tudor [40] and Canadair DC4Ms [41]. The Argentine used a similar engine in the Lincoln bomber [42]. A tremendous effort was made to make the Merlin successful commercially. However it was too small for the emerging airliners and with its military design concept it was a difficult task to achieve the lives demanded of civil engines and their major components. Its great virtue was that it gave Rolls-Royce a start in the civil market and taught the Company some hard lessons about being professional in the business which in the long term contributed to the success of the Dart. It also worried Pratt and Whitney sufficiently to make them introduce the R2184 at Merlin powers, and whose only home was the Saab Scandia. Unfortunately some of the lessons of the

Merlin were overlooked in later years and prejudiced the RB211 in the eyes of some potential customers.

Between 1939 and 1945 the Merlin saw operational service in 19 different types of aircraft plus large families of Spitfires and Mosquitoes. Ratings in service ranged from 1,000 horsepower to over 2,000 hp (Merlin 66, 1944). During the Battle of Britain the Merlin III gave 1,000 hp at 16,000 ft but by the middle of 1942 the Merlin 61 in squadron service in the Spitfire IX was giving this power at 30,000 ft and by mid 1944 the RM16SM (113/114) gave the same power at 36,000 ft. In 1945 the Merlin RM17SM had been type tested and flight tested at 2,200 hp (30 lb boost). It was only the end of the War that prevented this rating being used in service. The RM17SM was the only Merlin rating to use a camshaft change to increase power, having a longer duration exhaust cam. The Merlin also completed a short endurance test at 2,640 hp using 3,000 rpm and 36 lb boost with water injection. More important however were two 100 hr tests run at a continuous 3,000 rpm, +18 lb boost during the development of the Merlin 100 series.

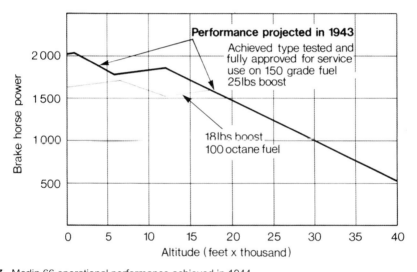

7   Merlin 66 operational performance achieved in 1944

Brake Horsepower per cubic inch had improved from 0.6 to over 1.24 for production engines (Merlin III to Merlin 100 series). For the same engine types specific weight, quoted as nett dry, had improved from 1.4 to 0.8 lb per horsepower.

The effect of this development work and its success is seen today in the pylon racing Merlin Mustangs in America. These engines, using largely standard Merlin parts from either late military or civil types, are reputed to be pulling 3,800 rpm and in the order of 135 inches boost, which is over 3,000 hp. The only major technical departure is the L section piston ring to reduce blow-by, a change which is worth about 300 hp.

The design and development effort to provide the Merlin with the power to give combat aircraft the necessary superiority led to 21 different power ratings and some 50 marks of engine to meet different installation needs. There were also about 1,000 modifications aimed at improving the breed or simplifying production. Associated with this was the learner curve of new production organisations and the suppliers supporting them. There was also the repair organisation of which the UK component was turning out over 1,000 engines per month including modification programmes and repair schemes.

Although the Merlin had been schemed as an air defence fighter engine, it was widely used in the Fairey Battle day bomber [43], outdated when the War started, and was also established as a heavy bomber engine in the Armstrong Whitworth Whitley IV and V [44] and the Vickers-Armstrong Wellington II [45] and four engined Handley Page Halifax [46]. Production of these types included 1,650 Whitleys, over 440 Wellingtons and around 3,000 Halifaxes. The problems of the Vulture in the Avro Manchester led to the decision to sideline the engine and use four Merlins to create the Lancaster of which 7,300 were built (300 with Hercules) [47]. This added more than 30,000 two-speed single stage engines to the programme at increasing power ratings.

The Mosquito, which had to overcome a great deal of opposition, started as an unarmed high speed bomber in which role it became outstanding [48]. Developments led to an effective fighter bomber and intruder, the RAF's best night fighter [49] and long range fighter, including in its tasks support for Bomber Command on night raids over Germany. Its versatility included Pathfinder operations, a photographic reconnaissance (PR) version and a development for shipping strikes. Over 7,700 aircraft were built.

The ubiquitous Spitfire operated in almost every role for a single engined aircraft, from a little known air-sea rescue version capable of dropping a dinghy pack and with a good low level performance to provide cover while rescue was effected, through the magnificent IX [51, 52] and XVI with the Merlin 66 and 266 which carried the brunt of the medium altitude fighting. High altitude operations employed the HF IX and pressure cabin mark VII powered by various high altitude Merlins but mainly 61s, 63s and RM11SM 70s. There were also PR versions and a few special

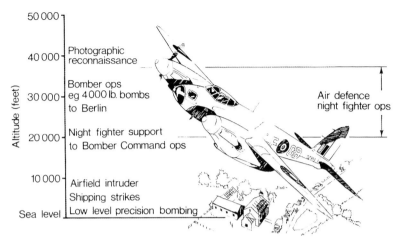

8 Typical Merlin Wartime 'Ops' – Mosquito

Mark VIIs which could operate at 47,000 ft. The great feature of the Spitfire apart from its flying capabilities was its ability to use all the power that Cyril Lovesey could get from the Merlin, turning the tables on the new Fw190 and Me109 developments. Over 18,500 Spitfires were built with Merlins to which may be added the Merlin Seafires bringing the total to over 20,000.

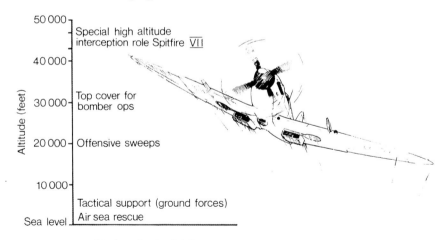

9 Typical Merlin Wartime 'Ops' – Spitfire

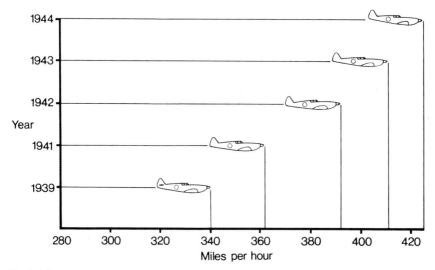

10 Spitfire speed increase due to Merlin development

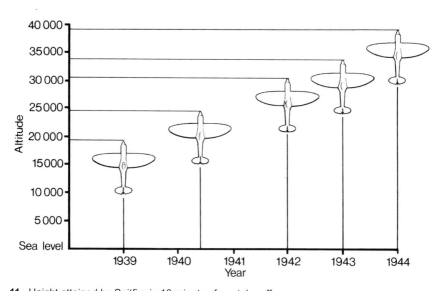

11 Height attained by Spitfire in 10 minutes from take-off

The Hurricane, having borne the brunt of the action in the Battle of Britain, continued to give sterling service in fighter and ground attack roles in many theatres of war. Its only engine variants were the Merlin XX and 22 and over 14,500 aircraft were produced [53, 54].

Packard engines in single stage form were used in some Lancasters and Mosquitoes and later versions of the Curtiss P40 [55]. However, the British initiative to use the two stage Packard Merlin in the North American Mustang turned what had been a rather modest performer with the Allison V1710 into a top class fighter and long range escort [56, 57]. Both P40s and Mustangs with Merlins were used widely by the American forces and the Mustang was regarded by some pilots as the best fighter the Americans had.

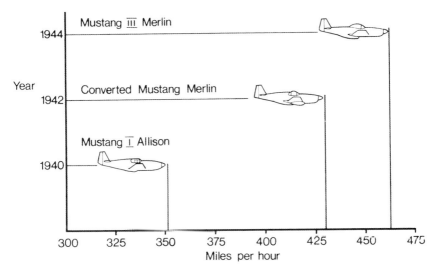

12 Mustang speed increase due to Merlin development

More than 12,000 Merlin Mustangs were built. The wartime total of Merlin powered single engined fighters exceeded 50,000 to which must be added small numbers of aircraft like the Fairey Barracuda dive bomber [58] and the Hawker Henley dive bomber, much superior to the Battle, but used only as a target tug.

Experience in service

The different aircraft types imposed many demands on the engine and some of the installations had powerful effects on engine reliability. The single engine installations were generally benign, as was the Lancaster, with its powerplants carried well forward of the wing and with their top line hardly breaking the leading edge. The greatest difficulties arose with the Halifax and Mosquito soon after entering service. The Halifax [59] gave many reduction gear problems. In one period of less than six months there were some 95 failures of reduction gears in the Halifax squadrons of which no fewer than 75 were in the port outer installation. During the same period the Lancaster squadrons suffered no more than a nominal number of the sort of casualties one would expect. Thus the Halifax problem appeared to be associated with the installation. The powerplant was set close to the wing and well above the leading edge so that there was a lot of disturbed airflow around the propellers. The three bladers used imposed a heavy vibration on the engine and a change was made to four bladed types. While this was not a complete cure it was an alleviation, but there was a shortage of propellers and one would therefore see Halifaxes with four bladers on the outer engines and three bladers on the inboards, and on occasion a four blader on the port outer only.

The Mosquito problem arose from the proximity of the propeller tips to the fuselage producing a first propeller order vibration causing reduction gear troubles. A great deal of design effort went into the engines for both aircraft types to make the reduction gears work reliably under the imposed loadings and this is discussed later in the text. The Mosquito problem would however respond to using increased rpm and it became practice to operate at 2,400 rpm or above when operations permitted.

Engines in these aircraft tended to suffer failures of the joint washers between the main structural joints. This was cured by deleting the washers on all engines and using the Alan Squires SQ jointing compounds. Alan was one of the characters of the Company and I regarded him as a mechanical chemist for his work on jointing compounds and cooling systems, all conducted from a tiny laboratory behind the technical block at Nightingale Road.

Hucknall played a key role in dealing with these problems and it is worth mentioning some of its activities which were so bound up in the history of the Merlin. In 1935 Ray Dorey (*Dor*) became general manager. He was one of those larger than life characters and having a geographically separate site put his own stamp on it. Hucknall had started as a flight test operation with an installation department to advise manufacturers on fitting Rolls-Royce engines with their liquid cooling systems. With the War it grew quickly and undertook a great deal of installation work as well as a greatly expanded test flying programme. The Merlin powerplant for the Lancaster was designed and built there but complete prototype installations were also carried out on site. These included the Griffon Beaufighter and Henley. Such were its facilities that during the Battle of Britain a Hurricane repair line was set up to help meet the needs of the RAF.

Hucknall's outstanding feat was to install a Merlin 65 in an existing Mustang and fly it in 3 months, beating North American Aviation who were doing the same thing on their own ground.

In an attempt to overcome the vibration problems on the Mosquito a flexible engine mount was designed, known as the Consus mounting, and was flown at Hucknall but did not reach production.

The same Mosquito was subsequently fitted with Rolls-Royce powerplants with chin radiators [60]. Tests before and after conversion using the same Merlin 23 engines and propellers showed no measurable difference in performance at the same all up weight. On calibration test flights the speed was 378 mph true at 18,000 ft at a weight of 18,400 lb.

The Flight Test unit under Capt Shepherd was like a small air force with a whole range of aircraft. During the War his pilots included Harvey Heyworth, L R Stokes (Stokey to his friends, awarded the DFC for daytime Blenheim operations in 1940 when he was 39), Robbie Robinson (an ex Imperial Airways pilot who used to three-point Lancasters), Reg Kirlew, "Suttey" Sutcliffe and Roscoe Turner. Also on the flying roster were flight engineers Joan McGowan and Olive Andrews. Jim Heyworth and Cliff Rogers, who is still flying as Company Chief of Flight Operations, were post War Chief Test Pilots. Both were very experienced Wartime bomber pilots and have contributed generously to the operational part of this account of the Merlin.

Combat aircraft were kept fully armed and this led to a typical 'Doreyesque' incident. Early in 1941 I was driving R W Harvey-Bailey (*By*) to Hucknall to see Dor when there was one of the few daylight raids that penetrated to the East Midlands. As we drove, shell bursts were very much in evidence and on arrival we found that Dor had scrambled Capt Shepherd, Reg Kirlew and Ronnie Harker, seconded back to the Company as a Liaison Pilot, to try and intercept the intruders. Without ground control Dorey's air force lost contact in cloud over the Wash and had to return.

Ronnie Harker was flying an ex squadron Hurricane in which he had carried out 150 consecutive rolls in an endeavour to reproduce the big end problems of early wartime Merlins because oil pressure dropped during the roll. As a result of this he had lost a bet with *By* who had said that this would not cause failure because of the oil remaining in the crankshaft. I had examined the engine after the episode and found the big ends perfect but the mains burnished as one would expect.

Following the meeting, *Dor* took *By* to show him an Allison powered P40, just delivered for a test flying programme. It was about contemporary with a Hurricane I but its armament was two .300 machine guns firing through the propeller in contrast with the twelve gun Hurricanes and cannon armed Spitfires then with the squadrons. Dor commented 'No test pilot flies it until it gets proper guns', and the events of the afternoon lent point to the remark.

The chilling part of this was that had Britain's fighters not been so effective and had industry not been able more than to make good the RAF's losses in the Battle of Britain, it would have been little use to have looked to the Americans in the Autumn of 1940 for a fighter which could have made a real contribution to the situation. In fact the only American fighters to reach a squadron before the Battle of Britain ended were some Grumman Martlets for the Fleet Air Arm in 804 Squadron operating under the control of 13 Group Fighter Command. These had been ordered by the Navy in 1939 and in consequence had a bullet proof windscreen, armour plating behind the pilot and four wing mounted machine guns instead of two in the fuselage. Like all Grumman aeroplanes they handled well and in the Navy were an advance over the Gloster Sea Gladiator and Fairey Fulmar. The Fulmar was a fighter version of the P4/34 light bomber and therefore not a fast or agile aeroplane with its single Merlin VIII or later the 100 octane rated Merlin 30, both these engines being moderately supercharged for Fleet Air Arm operation.

The Martlet was powered by a Wright R-1820 giving 1,000 hp at about 12,000 ft. While it was a capable Naval fighter, it could not have lived in the hot seat areas alongside the Hurricanes and Spitfires against the Me109s in the Battle. It was probably a good thing that the squadron was not operational until late October and was based at Wick. At that time American published performance figures were pretty optimistic but they learned the hard way, as they did in armament, profiting from British experience.

Fighter performance was always improving. In the latter part of the Battle, the Germans had some uprated 109s while as already mentioned the RAF had some Merlin XII powered Spitfire IIs and Merlin XX powered Hurricane IIs in the squadrons. The Merlin XII was a modest improvement on the Merlin III while the Merlin XX with its two-speed blower increased full throttle height by 25 per cent and power by about 12 per cent. Early in 1941 the Merlin 45 and 46 provided similar improvements in the Spitfire V [50].

The Germans were a resourceful enemy and although the Spitfire V could cope with the 109F the Germans replied with the 109G and the Fw190. The latter with its 42 litre, close cowled, geared fan cooled BMW801 radial could outrun and out climb the Spitfire V. The introduction of the various two stage supercharged Merlins in the Spitfire IX and later the XVI effectively countered the Fw190. These were followed by the more brutal looking Griffon versions with more speed and climb but perhaps lacking the balanced handling of the Merlin types. The Spitfire XIV with the two stage Griffon 64 was noted for its altitude performance, a characteristic enhanced by the Rotol five bladed propeller which was very efficient at height [**61**].

Reverting to the P40 at Hucknall, test flying did start but within a few weeks its Allison engine appeared in my section for investigation. All the big ends had gone and there had been a nasty fire, which suggested that other people had their troubles too.

Test flying was not, however, without real danger. The Vulture was undergoing an intensive flight programme and late in 1940 Reg Kirlew flying the big twin Vickers B1/35 experienced a major engine cooling system failure. This led to an uncontrolled engine fire with the cylinders burning like thermite. Kirlew, with a brilliant piece of flying, did a wheels down landing on the small grass airfield at Burnaston near Derby, thus preserving the evidence intact. Early in 1941 he was flying a Manchester when the same thing happened. Again, to try and save the evidence he attempted to land at RAF Ternhill with the whole powerplant ablaze. This time the gods were against him and the aircraft crashed and burned. Reg was killed and Flight Engineer Derek Broome survived with injuries. Five other personnel escaped.

The trouble was finally traced to a breakdown in the engine cooling flow. The Vulture had two coolant pumps dealing with each half of the engine but had no means of balancing the total flow. The trouble disappeared when a balance pipe was fitted across the coolant pump inlets.

Hucknall also housed the RAF liaison team who maintained close contact with the flying side of the RAF and to whom Hives (*Hs*) listened intently. They dealt with operating techniques, handling problems and represented to *Hs* troubles that were causing concern to the pilots. Many of the liaison pilots were Rolls-Royce personnel who, pre War, had been RAFVR or were RAux AF and who had been called up in 1939. A number had flown in the Battle of Britain and included Ronnie Harker, Harry Bailey (later to be Chief Test Pilot) Tony Martindale and Mike Royce, while Peter Birch and the racing driver Reggie Tongue came from outside the Company.

Martindale subsequently did the high Mach number dives in Spitfires at Farnborough reaching Mach 0.92. On the first dive the propeller could not control the engine and at something over 4,500 rpm the connecting rod bolts gave up. On the second dive over-revving again occurred and a propeller blade pulled out of the hub. The resultant out-of-balance force ripped the top half of the reduction gear from the engine, the whole lot leaving the aircraft. In both cases Martindale succeeded in landing the aircraft.

The Liaison Pilots were helpful in our failure investigation work, particularly when we were in real difficulty, maintaining a two way traffic of communication separate from formal channels. As an example, at the height of the Halifax reduction gear problems Ronnie Harker was able to fly me to 4 Group headquarters at York and to visit some of the worst affected stations including Elvington, Breighton, Rufforth and Holme-on-Spalding Moore in the course of one Saturday. This enabled me to brief the Senior Air Staff Officer, the Group Engineering Officer, station officers and squadron pilots. Aided by Ronnie I was able to put over the problems and the action being taken, and re-establish confidence which had been on the wane. It also enabled us to get Group to press from its end for four bladed propellers which were a quick alleviation to the problem.

Operational Flying

There is no question that the Merlin was a pilot's engine. During the War, I rubbed shoulders with many pilots and have recently taken the opportunity of talking to a number who are still around. Through all their comments runs a common thread – the ability of the engine to run continuously at high power and, if an engine did fail for some reason, the other or others would pick up the load and run on, if need be, way outside operational limitations. A few quotes illustrate this:

'I had to return from Nuremburg in a Wellington II on one engine and used maximum boost and revs on a Merlin X for five hours with no sign of distress'

The Captain of Lord Mountbatten's York:
'We struck the most appalling weather with extraordinary icing condtions. To maintain height I had to use 2,850 rpm +12 lb for three hours'.

Fighter Pilot:
'The engine was just part of the kit and one never doubted that it would continue to run whatever you did with it'.

Finally, the confidence of a Lancaster captain who lost an engine on climb out and pressed on to bomb Stuttgart using climb power on three engines for the whole trip.
 It was also a simple engine to manage and this, with its ability to perform, added to its reputation. It must be remembered that Bomber Command suffered over 55,000 air crew casualties in its European offensive and pilots could be on operations with no more than 160 hours in their log books, so it had to be easy to handle and tolerant of the treatment it got.

For four long years Bomber Command was the only truly offensive arm that Britain had to take the war to Germany. Over the length of the War the Merlin provided the power to deliver the major tonnage of bombs dropped on Germany by the RAF. In the early days of the War, the Whitley V was the only bomber the RAF had which was capable of crossing the Alps with a war load to attack Italian industry.

In terms of operating techniques a typical Whitley V or Wellington II operation would be to take off at 3,000 rpm with +5 lb boost, climbing en route at 2,600 rpm using 4 lb boost with weak mixture. There would be a shift into FS gear* and cruise at 17,000 ft at 2,000 to 2,400 rpm and between zero and +2 lb boost. Later in the War, Merlin 24 operation in a Lancaster would be take-off at 3,000 rpm, +18 lb boost. This would be reached within 100 yards of the start of the take-off run and most of a 2,000 yard runway would be required to get airborne with Berlin the target and an 8,000 lb bomb load. Take-off power would be held until the aircraft was clean and settled in the climb then throttled to 2,850 rpm and +9 lb boost with 12 lb as a contingency. On reaching operating height, which would be around 20,000 ft depending on aircraft weight and other factors, 2,650 rpm, +6 or 7 lb boost, FS gear in weak mixture would be used for cruise. Pilots would aim for as high an altitude as possible and 22,000 ft was not unknown as a cruising height. Equally, return altitude would be as high as reduced weight allowed. The important issues were time on target and staying with ones aircraft wave. Being a straggler increased the risk of being shot down by about 60 per cent.

In the commercial world engine management is all important but no resemblance exists between the calm of the civil flight deck and the cockpit of a heavy bomber with its young crew flying into the teeth of determined enemy opposition. In a crisis of combat damage or evasive action the engines just had to keep going at whatever power was demanded and, provided a sick engine would give power and was not a danger to the aircraft, it was kept running. Completion of the mission and safe return were all important. As one pilot said 'If we had to, we ran the Merlin with all the needles hard on the righthand stops'.

In fighter operations conditions were much more variable particularly in air to air combat when a pilot would use maximum combat power for as long as he had to, which could be as much as 25 lb boost on two stage engines. Early in the War there was no set handling technique and most pilots flew where the engine felt happiest at or above 2,400 rpm.

There was an operational reason for this. Before the days of inter-connected throttle and speed control it was necessary to advance the speed lever (pitch control) before opening the throttle, and the higher the initial rpm the better the response. Later in the War if following the technique of high boost/low rpm for range flying, it

---

*Supercharger drive speeds; MS – moderate speed, FS – full speed.

was vital to advance the speed lever before the throttle, otherwise acceleration would be ruined which could be fatal when bounced by the enemy.

As it became necessary to strike deeper into enemy territory more attention was paid to range flying and the technique of high boost/low revs (7 lb boost at 1,800 rpm) became more commonly used. While it undoubtedly produced the best economy there were a number of side effects. It was generally unloved by pilots who preferred the sweeter feel of the engine at higher revs. Because it raised piston temperatures and reduced the hammering loads on the piston rings, it tended to promote ring gumming with the risk of oil consumption, and piston troubles, particularly on engines at long lives.

Nonetheless the technique of running the engine at full throttle and controlling boost by revs at altitude was correct. Fortuitously speed, weight and altitude often led to a good compromise. Thus the high altitude Mosquito bomber taking a 4,000 lb bomb to Berlin would be run with the engines at full throttle at 2,300 rpm which gave about 4 lb boost at 30,000 ft. This was a good cruising regime for the aircraft and gave close to 360 mph true airspeed. Such was the performance of the Mosquito that one aircraft could undertake two sorties to Berlin in one night.

Air Marshal Sir Ivor Broom, a very experienced Mosquito pilot, gives an interesting sidelight on this. He completed 25 sorties to Berlin flying single stage engined Mosquitoes. Operating from Cambridgeshire airfields the average on the ground to on the ground time was 4¼ hours. One of the squadron's saying was 'Berlin and back and in the bar before it closes'.

Heavy bomber operation over Europe could be affected by the prevailing westerly winds which could be a hazard to returning aircraft. Unforecasted winds of 125 knots were a substantial cause of heavy losses during the big Nuremburg raid, when a number of returning aircraft were forced down in the North Sea due to lack of fuel. This emphasised the need for range flying techniques which led to the crew room doggerel:

> *Don't fly at night either fast or slow,*
> *With your revs too high or your boost to low,*
> *Or you will run out of gas with a long way to go,*
> *and you won't get home in the morning.*

When intercooled engines came into service it was found that low charge temperatures which occurred at high altitude and low rpm gave rise to plug leading. This was not so serious on Spitfire operations but on the Mustang, undertaking escort duties with the USAAF on long-range daylight penetration raids, it was vital to fly at high boost/low revs to get the range. On such flights it was necessary to open up the engine periodically to clear the plugs and retain combat capability.

The versatile Mosquito produced some interesting facets of Merlin operation. In September 1942, MP469 fitted with Merlin 61s and flying at a low weight reached 42,000 ft with a rate of climb of 500 feet per minute still available. The RAF at this time were concerned over a few very high altitude penetrations by single Ju86P aircraft which had not been successfully intercepted. The performance of MP469 led to the production of four lightweight MkXV aircraft, carrying only two machine guns and powered by Merlin 72/73s. These aircraft were allocated to Wing Commander John Cunningham's 85 Squadron at Hunsdon with the object of intercepting these high flying raiders, but it is evident that the enemy was having difficulty with the Ju86P and the raids ceased.

As far as the Mosquito was concerned, priority for two stage engines went to the MkIX bomber and the MkXVI PR aircraft, both high altitude types.

The brunt of the night fighting was carried by the single stage engined Mosquitoes, latterly powered by Merlin 25s. These aircraft did well but the margin of performance over the Me410 could make interception more difficult. Two aircraft were modified at Farnborough to provide nitrous oxide injection to boost engine power and provide an extra 40 knots plus at 28,000 ft for about six minutes. On the night of January 2/3 1944 John Cunningham, flying HK374, a modified aircraft, shot down an Me410 off Le Touquet. Fifty MkXIIIs were modified with nitrous oxide injection for 410 and 96 squadrons. Engines which had run around 200 hours with the use or nitrous oxide were found to be in excellent condition. In the middle of 1944 the first Mk30 night fighters, with two stage high altitude engines and more power, reached the squadrons [**62**]. In the autumn Mk34 PR aircraft powered by Mk113/114 engines, the ultimate in Merlin high altitude performance, became operational. These engines, with the more efficient supercharger having an overhung first stage impeller and single-point fuel injection into the eye of the supercharger, gave 800 hp at 40,000 ft. Bomber and fighter versions with these engines did not reach the squadrons in time to go into action.

The first service use of Merlin 100 series engines was early in 1944 when five special aircraft were built by de Havillands. These were MkXVI aircraft, which besides the new engine had extended wings for high altitude flying and were known as Mk32 and provided valuable experience with the fuel injected engines on PR operations.

While on the subject of flying characteristics and pilots' attitudes, the Beaufighter comes to mind [**63**]. It was Hercules powered, except for the MkII which was fitted with Merlin XXs in Rolls-Royce powerplants. It developed the reputation of being a 'vicey' aeroplane to fly with a tendency to swing at take-off, a feature common to some extent in all Beaufighters. I have been over this ground with Athol McIntyre who had been a Beaufighter II pilot and he did not regard it as being particularly vicey. Powered by the Merlin XX it had less take-off power than the Hercules version and needed more runway to develop good aerodynamic control speed. On the other hand, it had more altitude power but needed to be flown at high boost and revs to make it perform. He attributed his tolerance of the aircraft to having come to it from single engine equipment whereas the majority of Beaufighter II pilots had come from Beaufighters with Hercules engines which had opposite propeller rotation and therefore swung in the opposite direction.

I was involved with one Beaufighter squadron that was unhappy because of problems which had arisen with some early production engines. As a result of this they had missed a number of sorties against the enemy due to engine difficulties. As the problems were of a random nature some engines were changed in favour of later production units with more experience behind them and a higher mod status, and the trouble went away.

One criticism levelled at the Merlin was that its cooling system made it more vulnerable than an aircooled powerplant. This may be true, but while an aircooled engine could be kept running with powerplant damage it was the Merlin's ability to run for long periods outside operational limits, without risk of overheating and seizure, which was its strength. It could also operate at higher altitudes which reduced the risk of hits on the aircraft. The enemy had a high content of liquid cooled engines, in their front line equipment and even the Fw190 had a long nosed liquid cooled version with either Junkers Jumo or Daimler Benz powerplants, a few of which were seen later in the War.

Group Captain Cunningham comments that the Mosquito leading edge radiators were liable to damage under particular circumstances. In night interceptions particularly of Fw190s, having been radar vectored, one had to pick up the aircraft visually. The small silhouette from behind made it a difficult target and one homed on its exhaust flame. It was very difficult to judge range and it was common for fire to be opened at below 100 yards and sometimes at as little as 50 yards. The initial cannon shell strikes would produce a burst of debris in the form of shattered sheet metal and jagged pieces of perspex from the canopy, through which one had to fly, and these could pierce a radiator before the enemy fell away and crashed. He goes on to say that an aircooled engine would not have suffered in these conditions but the Hercules Beaufighter had neither the speed nor the altitude performance to intercept and destroy aircraft like the Fw190 so it was not really an issue.

Before the War the Company had set up an aero instruction school to train service and civilian personnel on its products. As the War progressed and the use of the Merlin became widespread a need arose for the pilots' course on engine handling to familiarise them with engine developments and the latest handling techniques, to get the best results in practice. The course was run by experienced RAF pilots on rest between operational tours. Courses proved to be a two way trade because, apart from the training aspects, pilots wished to talk over engine problems and would on occasion ask what had gone wrong with a specific engine. At this time the senior course instructor was Athol McIntyre and on every course I would go along to an open session when problems would be discussed. Because we were frank about our troubles we got a good response and learned things which were of value to us. The course then began to receive pilots with little experience of the Merlin, generally those converting to Mosquitoes and Lancasters. Rightly, they had a lot of brand loyalty, and with their unfamiliarity, they were subject to some hairy stories about the difficulties they were going to encounter with this small highly boosted liquid cooled engine, which grew like a Tarasconade with the telling. Mac soon found the response required a special technique, the immediate move being to praise whatever they were flying and then to draw out the virtues of their new equipment in the context of its role and the ability the Merlin gave it to meet a new enemy initiative.

  Rubbing shoulders with experienced Merlin pilots with their confidence had its effects and at the end of the course, one would find enthusiasm rather than anxiety. High boosts did take some getting across, particularly with American pilots who were used to large moderately boosted engines and using inches of mercury absolute as a measure. 80 in seemed an impossibly high number to them as did 25 lb and Harker suggested that boost gauges should be calibrated in stones to reduce the scale.

The drive for improvements

Having said this, the Merlin, like all engines, had its moments which arose from many sources. The response was to attack the trouble either by engineering action, remedial action on production and repair, or by getting to grips with maintenance or operating problems in the squadrons. When an epidemic did break out Hives was not the man to let the aircrews sweat it out. There were times when, in consultation with the Service and the Ministries, the most affected squadrons were campaigned to fit the best standard of engine that could be mustered. This not only improved morale but rapidly evaluated the action taken. This attitude applied in many ways. During the Battle of Britain part of the experimental shop was turned over to engine repairs to increase output. When the Spitfire V was having a hard time with the

Fw190, production of the two stage supercharged Merlin 61 was brought forward and Hucknall shared with Vickers in the conversion of a number of Spitfire Vs to IXs. Thus the first Merlin 61 was ready for despatch on Christmas day, 1941, and 64 Squadron was operational with Spitfire IXs in July 1942.

One of the less successful campaigns in quest of power was the cropping of the supercharger rotor on Merlin 45s and 46s to give 18 lb boost at low level. This was intended to improve performance in the close support role during the forthcoming invasion of France. The aircraft concerned were Spitfire Vs which had their wings clipped by removal of the elliptical tips [64]. The campaign was carried out in advance of D-Day and the aircraft for a time were used in various roles, particularly at higher altitudes where they suffered badly. Both the engines and aircraft were somewhat tired, hence the soubriquet of "Clipped, cropped and clapped" and they were not popular with the pilots.

Service troubles had to be quickly dealt with and, in spite of much increased engine duty, lives had to be extended without losing reliability to make the best use of available equipment and ease demands on spares and shop facilities.

To appreciate what was involved, one must look at how the organisation developed to handle its many new tasks and build close relationships with the Services. Design and Development had to meet the need of the Services, and in particular the RAF, in developing engines capable of achieving technical and operational superiority over the enemy. Also to be able to respond to new situations arising from the technical initiative of a determined and resourceful adversary. This stretched what would now be called Engineering, but the results speak for themselves. Production had an equally difficult task to meet the quantity, quality and changing product demands in the climate of a massive expansion programme. Prior to the War the majority of operations in aero manufacture, build and test had been skilled in both a Trade Union and actual sense. In Derby, after almost a quarter of a century of the business growing up with the workforce, the true skills had become ingrained and many vital bits of knowledge were almost part of the atmosphere in which people worked and often not formally documented.

With the development of the new factories, men and women had to be trained to make and repair aero engines in areas where the skills were not endemic. Union rules and demarcations had to be eased by dilution agreements, and such were the aptitudes of the British that all over the country the so called butchers, bakers and candlestick makers and their wives and girl friends increased the trickle of engines to a river of power. Women worked not only in terms of manual tasks, but in draughting and many other skills. Air Transport Auxiliary girls flew everything there was to fly, including all the Merlin powered aircraft, as a routine.

The new factories with very small nuclei of experienced personnel became the major source of engines and they had their problems exacerbated by their growing pains. Derby, also with a high degree of dilution and the new suppliers, took on the initial runs of advanced types.

To handle these new problems there had to be a third force and, like Topsy, it just 'growed' to meet the needs. These were:

1. To deal with non-conformance problems by finding out how to use material in this category while maintaining product integrity and avoiding a repetition by working with production and inspection.

2. To ease Production's tasks by simplifying designs without losing performance or reliability, by means of a Production Development team.

3. To develop a Repair Engineering group to provide 'know how' to the rapidly expanding repair organisation in the form of standards, repair schemes and methods. Also to ensure that modification programmes to improve the breed were comprehensible to production and repair and to develop salvage of existing parts where possible in such programmes.

4. To set up an Engine Defect Investigation Unit to ensure that engines were not only effectively investigated but that prompt follow-up action was taken in terms of Engineering, Quality and Production or with the Services should in-field or operational procedures be involved. This section worked in close rapport with the Aero Service Department which provided support to, and liaison with, the RAF via its service representatives in the field

This was set in motion by R W Harvey-Bailey (*By*) and subsequently by J D (later Sir Denning) Pearson in Scotland, who also handled the Packard Merlin. Crewe came under the aegis of *By* who also maintained close links with Ford. On their own staff Ford and Alf Vickers from Rolls-Royce to provide technical management.

These different activities tended to complement each other and the engine by its characteristics helped the situation. Unlike the gas turbine whose technology is associated with parts that have a minimum of rubbing contact and material characteristics of very specialised natures, a piston engine had a concentration of impacting and rubbing surfaces. Materials were more basic and one learned by examining components and understanding what the various bedding and wear patterns told one.

At the start of a new factory or new engine type, all engines were endurance tested, stripped and rebuilt for final test. As engine conditions permitted this was eased until only a sample of engines were stripped, the remainder being endurance final tested and, if satisfactory, despatched. This system was no formality. One would find very senior people on the inspection lines seeing for themselves. At the time a number of features, such as reduction gear tip correction and tooth alignment, was determined almost entirely by bedding patterns. Bearings, pistons and rings, and joint conditions would be looked at critically and, if warnings were present of impending trouble, action would be initiated. Later in the War, Production Proof Tests were introduced when sample engines from the line would be subjected to the last 25 hours of the type test and then examined with the object of seeing troubles that might not show on normal non-easement engines. If one reads this in context with the failure investigation activity and the monitoring of repair engine condition, and recognising the short timescales involved, it will be seen that there was an effective system for handling the situation.

As Derby built pilot quantities of major new types, various parameters including final performance limits and such things as piston profiles, ring gaps and other features would be established on production, not without some lively and competitive arguments with other interested parties.

The Production Development team, in addition to proof testing, ran engines to clear production easements, major salvage and repair schemes as well as some competitive design efforts like big oil pumps. In terms of savings in man hours, by clearing major salvage and non-conformance issues, over 2.5 million man hours were saved by testing on one engine (WT2). A number of quite major changes to aid Production were also cleared, for example, dechambering of crank and propeller and other shaft bores, solid supercharger clutch plates and the simplified upper vertical drive, the latter two also improving service reliability.

As an example of the needs of wartime operation, a repair scheme for crankcases cracked in forced landings was also cleared. It was common for a forced landing to crack the crankcase at the junction of the reduction gear housing to the body of the crankcase. The scheme involved welding of the cracks under controlled conditions and the fitting of a steel tie rod between the housing and crankcase spine. This scheme must have saved hundreds of crankcases.

A much needed by-product of this operation was the issue of more formal documentation to transmit information not carried by drawings or other means.

Technical Instructions covered a raft of information affecting both new production and repair, including executive instructions.

Engine Repair Memoranda were essentially repair documents, providing technical standards, instructions covering the repair of specific items and guidance on issues such as interchangeability of important components.

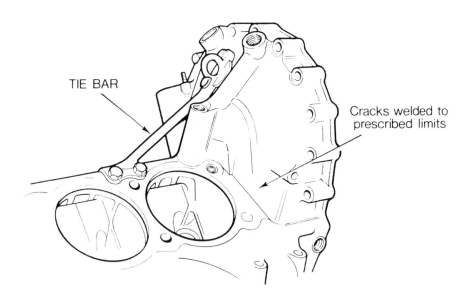

TIE BAR

Cracks welded to prescribed limits

13 Wartime crankcase repair following crash landing

Salvage schemes were based on RSc's and WR schemes, which carried full Company and Ministry approval.

ENGINE REPAIR MEMORANDUM
ISSUED BY
ROLLS-ROYCE LIMITED, DERBY

E.R.M. II4.

SUBJECT :—
MERLIN CONNECTING RODS.

BY/HB.1/IH.4.11.44.

Sft.   Sft 'Thn   TB/GAC.

Sft. LA
Sft NP
Sft LA GW
Sft LA CH   } Nottingham
Sft LA FH } Cyl
Sft LA GH } blocks

al   BY/Mx
S.. MC   BY/AS
Sft/CLH.   NW
TB/Pkn.   CB/CM.
TB/CPJ   E TGD.
TB/AFW   HPS/CS
TB/Wkn
Sft/Hd., Bilborough.

Mr. Baker, R.T.O.
I 1/c A.I.D., Derby

Mr Nichols, R.T.O., Glasgow

Psn GJ } Glasgow
M. EC.

Gnr., Crewe.

Vks , Ford Co.

Bk CP } Hyde {Cyl
I 1/c A I D } Road {Blocks.

I 1/c A I D., Nottingham.
I 1/c A I D., Sunbeam-Talbot.
I 1/c A I D., de Havilland
I 1/c A I D., Alvis
I 1 c A I D., Glasgow
I 1 c A I D., Crewe
I 1 c A I.D., Ford Co
I 1 c A I D., Dumbristle
I 1 c A I D., Fleetlands
C.I.O., No. 31 M.U.
S A I., 43 Group.

Mr Poppe, Sunbeam-Talbot.

Mr Kennedy, de Havilland.

Mr. Vaux, Alvis, Staffs.

O C., H Q., 43 Group.

C. I O., No. 31 M.U.
O C , E R S , No. 31 M.U.

Mr Scholes, c/o TB AFW
Mr Devey, c/o TB/AFW
Mr Simmonds, c/o TB/AFW.
Sgt. Leech, c/o TB/AFW
Mr. Blue, c/o Glasgow Liaison
Office.
Mr Ellis (Naval Liaison)

R. .HF.
Km /Mdx.

D D R.M. (M.A.P.)
D S M. (A.M.)

R D E. /2   R.Q.E./M2.

Dir A.M R., Admiralty.

Air Material, Admiralty.

Chief Naval Representative
(M.A.P.)

R T.P.7.

M   Tata Ltd.

The Metal Box Co. Ltd.,
Bradford.

A number of failures of forked connecting rods on the Merlin engine in Service have been typified by a characteristic fatigue fracture at the bolt lugs, the initial crack emanating from the inner edges of the lugs at the point where the lug runs into the base of the rod. To overcome this fault an improved design has been brought into production under Mod. 587 which is known as the "blended radius rod", and has no serious stress concentration around the bolt lugs.

It should, however, be emphasised that the critical factor in the original and Mod. 399 designs is connected with the finish along the edges of the lugs, particularly where the lug joins the rod, and for some time past, a .030+10 radius has been called for with a view to setting a tangible standard of quality. The purpose of this note is to draw attention to the radius in question, and render it a feature for examination during overhaul when the rods have been removed from the crankshaft. The essential factor is that the radius must be true and run out smoothly; a curved chamfer merely shifts the dangerous stress concentration inwards a little, without attacking the problem.

The evidence made available during defect investigation indicates that adherence to this instruction will prevent Service failures attributable to this cause as many engines are still equipped with pre-Mod. 587 rods, which have functioned with complete satisfaction, and it is only isolated rods, in relation to the number produced, which have given trouble.

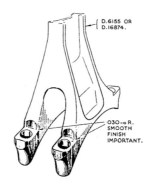

D.6155 OR
D.16874.

030 +0 R.
SMOOTH
FINISH
IMPORTANT.

BY/HB.

14 Sample repair instruction

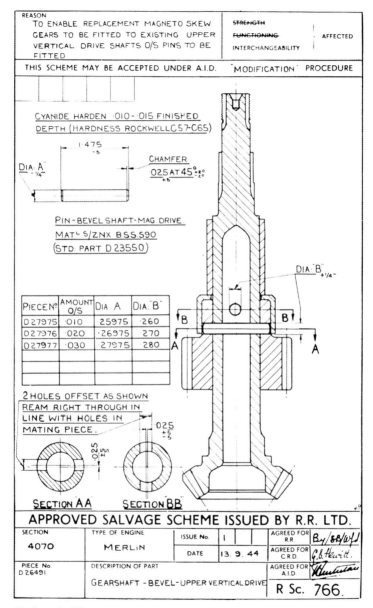

REASON
TO ENABLE REPLACEMENT MAGNETO SKEW
GEARS TO BE FITTED TO EXISTING UPPER
VERTICAL DRIVE SHAFTS O/S PINS TO BE
FITTED

STRENGTH
FUNCTIONING
INTERCHANGEABILITY — AFFECTED

THIS SCHEME MAY BE ACCEPTED UNDER A.I.D. MODIFICATION PROCEDURE

CYANIDE HARDEN ·010 - ·015 FINISHED
DEPTH (HARDNESS ROCKWELL C57-C65)

1·475
-5

DIA· A
- ¼

CHAMFER
·025 AT 45° +2°/-2°
+6

PIN - BEVEL SHAFT - MAG DRIVE.
MATL S/ZNX B.S.S.S90
(STD. PART D23550)

DIA· B
+¼

PIECE N°	AMOUNT O/S	DIA A	DIA· B
D27975	·010	·25975	·260
D27976	·020	·26975	·270
D27977	·030	·27975	·280

B B

A   A

2 HOLES OFFSET AS SHOWN
REAM RIGHT THROUGH IN
LINE WITH HOLES IN
MATING PIECE.

·025
+5
-5

·025
+5
-5

SECTION AA   SECTION BB

APPROVED SALVAGE SCHEME ISSUED BY R.R. LTD.

SECTION 4070	TYPE OF ENGINE MERLIN	ISSUE No.	I		AGREED FOR R.R.	By/SR/WJ
		DATE	13. 9. 44		AGREED FOR C.R.D.	G.S.Hewitt.
PIECE No. D26491	DESCRIPTION OF PART GEARSHAFT - BEVEL- UPPER VERTICAL DRIVE				AGREED FOR A.I.D.	Durstau

R Sc. 766.

15 Sample RSc

35

The Defect Investigation Unit was also responsible for the Monthly Review of Repair Engines. This document dealt with the highlight technical items on engines passing through the repair organisation in any one month, plus statistics:

a Total number of engines (around 1,000)
b Percentage of total time expired
c Percentage of failed engines
d Percentage of crashes and other causes (eg enemy action)
e Average life of engines reported on (the general mortality figure), broken down into the various categories (eg fighter and bomber)

This report had to be issued within four weeks of the end of the calendar month in question and was used, among other things, in the life extension programme. It was found that if a third of the engines in any category were reaching time expiry and the mortality figure was 60 per cent of the nominal life, it was time to consider a life increase, providing defect investigation and repair line monitoring showed no unusual trends. Each new major engine mark started at some agreed nominal so that there was always an active life extension in being.

What then were the main service problems encountered?

Backfires
When the Merlin entered the squadrons, the first trouble was backfiring, the results of which could range from a carburettor fire on start-up to an engine cut at take-off. The cure was to fit flame traps in the induction pipes as a field modification. These were made by Amal and consisted of a pack of foils, alternately plain and corrugated, which cooled the flame of a backfire, rather like a Davy lamp, stopping the mass of compressed mixture in the trunk pipe and supercharger from burning. This cured the immediate problem but led to other difficulties which are dealt with later.

Bearings
Bearing reliability was the next issue. At the outbreak of war, difficulty was being experienced in meeting the terminal velocity dive requirement of 3,600 rpm for 20 seconds. This had to be cleared by a 15 minute increment at the end of the type test running at 3,600 rpm with minimum load on the engine. Lubrication was marginal

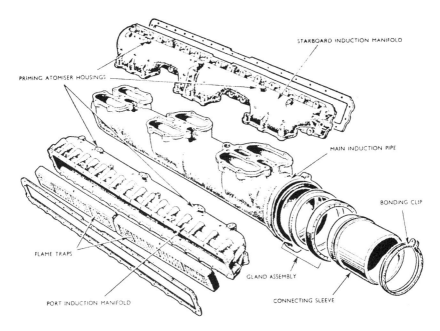

STARBOARD INDUCTION MANIFOLD

PRIMING ATOMISER HOUSINGS

MAIN INDUCTION PIPE

BONDING CLIP

FLAME TRAPS

GLAND ASSEMBLY

PORT INDUCTION MANIFOLD

CONNECTING SLEEVE

16 Induction manifolds

and if the test was completed, both big-ends and mains were angry and burnished. Combat experience confirmed this with a number of big-end failures, generally in numbers 3 and 4 positions. It was clear that oil flows had to be increased and a 30 per cent bigger pump stack was designed. This was done by boring the casings and designing new larger gears, cutting one less tooth than normal for the blank. This produced big tooth spaces with short pitch contacts to reduce oil trapping, and in consequence the power to drive the pumps. The pump speed was also increased by 10 per cent.

The Merlin system was a conventional gallery feed, oil being fed from holes in the main bearing caps not only to lubricate the mains, but via grooves in the shells and holes in the journals, to feed the big-ends via internal drillings. Thus numbers 1, 2, 5 and 6 big-ends were fed from continuous grooves in 2 and 6 mains. Numbers 3 and 4 big-ends were fed from partial grooves in 3 and 5 mains.

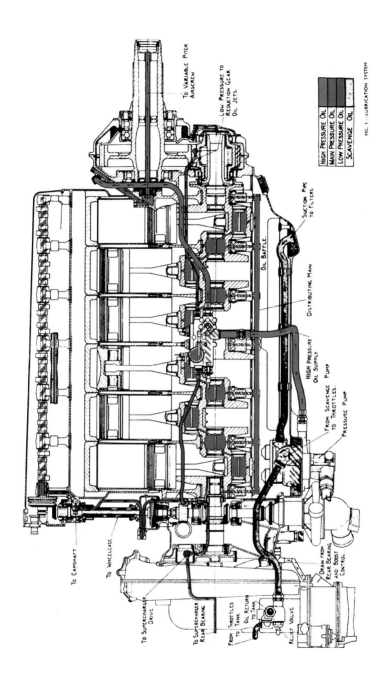

TO VARIABLE PITCH
AIRSCREW

LOW PRESSURE TO
REDUCTION GEAR
OIL JETS.

	HIGH PRESSURE OIL
	MAIN PRESSURE OIL
	LOW PRESSURE OIL
	SCAVENGE OIL

FIG. 1—LUBRICATION SYSTEM

SUCTION PIPE
TO FILTERS

OIL BAFFLE.

DISTRIBUTING MAIN

HIGH PRESSURE
OIL SUPPLY

FROM SCAVENGE PUMP
TO THROTTLES.

PRESSURE PUMP

TO CAMSHAFT

TO WHEELCASE

DRAIN FROM
REAR BEARING
AND BOOST
CONTROL

TO SUPERCHARGER
DRIVE.

TO SUPERCHARGER
REAR BEARING

FROM
THROTTLES
TO TANK.

OIL RETURN
TO TANK.

RELIEF VALVE

38

17 Conventional oil system

The bigger flows enabled the terminal velocity test to be passed easily but did not completely eliminate the service problem. However, having much more oil to play with, numbers 3 and 5 mains were given continuous grooves and a second oil hole was drilled in the crankpin at 180° to the existing single hole. These mods (266 and 283) fixed the problem. Interestingly enough, this package followed almost precisely the action taken to cure high-speed big-end failures on the 4¼ litre Bentley in 1937.

Main bearings were also in trouble. Two types of lead-bronze were available; one with ½ per cent silver and the other with 1 per cent tin. The former had good anti-seize properties but was prone to fail in fatigue within the bronze and just above the bond with the steel shell. The latter had good mechanical integrity but would seize under poor lubrication. A lubrication weakness lay in the number 4 main and the problem had been got around by using 1 per cent tin on all but the centre bearing where ½ per cent silver was used. Naturally this caused rejections for metal in the filters and the odd crank failure due to the journal being unsupported. The answer lay in improved lubrication, and this was done by putting partial grooves in the main bearing shells, drilling the crankshaft with two opposite holes and sealing the journal with caps. Around each oil hole flats were formed with carefully feathered trailing edges. Oil was thus forced under pressure into the journal while the holes were in contact with grooves and then centrifuged out via the flats when the bearing was heavily loaded. This was successful and enabled 1 per cent tin lead-bronze to be reinstated (Mod 194).

This was part of the lubrication package as it followed immediately on the big oil pumps. Significantly it was possible to modify existing cranks without re-nitriding following the various drilling operations. Basic crankshafts modified to this standard were used on all conventional feed engines and worked happily at over 2,000 hp on the Merlin 66.

Occasionally number 1 or 7 main would seize immediately after installation. This was thought to be due to a pocket of air getting into the bearings from the aircraft system. This was overcome by putting grooves in the backs of the shells feeding two extra holes in the upper halves. A temporary oil shortage is far less damaging than an oil shortage caused by air in the system being blown across the bearing. Tests on a centre bearing showed that at 3,000 rpm a bearing would run for 15 seconds after the oil was cut off before the temperature started to rise. However, if at the moment of cutting the oil supply, air was blown into the bearing, seizure was almost instantaneous.

Subsequently all bearings were lead plated to improve anti-seizure properties and Packard engines used silver-lead, ultimately changing to British practice.

The only continuing problem with main bearings was scoring and tearing due to circulation of foreign matter. Sometimes this was generated within the engine (eg heavy plucking of bevel gear teeth) but more often from installation contamination. No one would consider a fine pressure filter, but there was a rule of changing oil coolers and flushing the system following an engine change.

When the Merlin 100 series was designed, an end-to-end oil system was introduced. Oil was fed via transfer tubes into both ends of the crank, allowing all main bearing oil grooves to be deleted. The end feed system gives a much better control and distribution of oil flows through main and big-end bearings. By using stand-pipes in the journals the crank was its own centrifuge and trapped foreign matter before it could reach the bearings. Experience showed this scheme to be completely effective [**18**, page 43].

The lubrication changes had a powerful effect on reliability but it will be realised that with the sheer size of production, the learner curve of new factories and suppliers, coupled with increased power outputs all led to various parts of the engine giving some sort of trouble.

In failure investigation, we had one rule: 'There is no such thing as an isolated failure. The isolated failure of today is the epidemic of tomorrow'. This meant that every new failure had to be investigated and acted on, no matter what the previous history might be.

Service lives

In the context of service problems life extensions were kept under review but it was on very few occasions that a life extension planned had to be checked or postponed. So it was that in fighters, in spite of doubling combat power, life went from 240 hours to 300 hours, and in the case of twins as high as 360 hours. In bombers, 300 hours was extended to 420 hours on the Merlin 24 while 360 hours was the norm for earlier marks. At the end of the War, the early transport engines reached 480 to 500 hours.

Increases in overhaul life were achieved not only in conjunction with power increases but also in very significant gains in power-to-weight ratio due to design and development efforts.

Experience on the rest of the engine can be summarised as follows:

Supercharger and carburation

There were four basic superchargers used on the Merlin with many variations in gear ratios and rotor diameters to achieve the required horsepower and/or altitude performance. The original single stage Merlin used the side entry supercharger which was fitted with a twin choke SU carburettor. Except for a few impeller failures cured by changing the forging technique, it gave little trouble. The rotor was carried at its rear end in a plain tail bearing consisting of a fixed bronze bush in the rear half casing in which ran a floating steel bush. There was a further floating bronze bush between the tail journal and the steel bush. Lubrication was by spiral grooves, and it worked remarkably well apart from the fact that we were conscious of variations in tail end bearing oil consumption, by the amount of oil that was being seen in superchargers.

The front ball bearing was a typical bronze cage bearing with the cage located on the inner race and, right through the history of the engine, on all superchargers casualties did occur. The first change was from a cast to a forged silicon-bronze cage followed by an increased capacity bearing (Mod 430). As an alternative to the Hoffman bearing, a Fischer type was used with a ribbon steel cage running on the balls. A feature of the Fischer bearing was that, having fewer but larger diameter balls than its bronze cage counterpart, it had better load capacity and was more reliable in service. It was always felt that the lubrication of the bronze cage on the

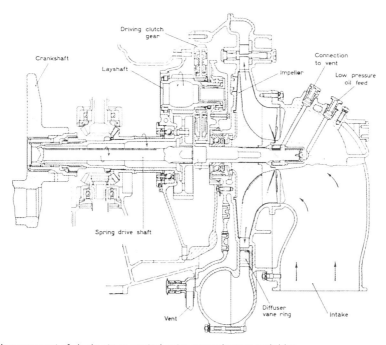

19 Arrangement of single stage central entry supercharger and drive

41

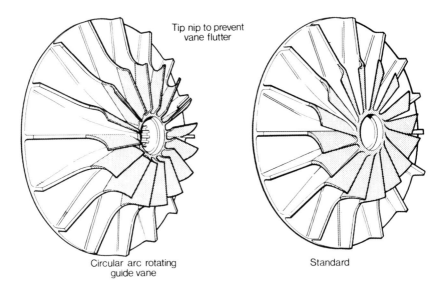

Tip nip to prevent
vane flutter

Circular arc rotating
guide vane

Standard

20 Supercharger rotors

inner race on the side remote from the oil feed could be suspect, a feature which did not apply with the steel cage where the natural centrifuge effect through the bearing tended to spread the oil more evenly. Effort was needed however to maintain the standard of finish on the steel cages. Finally, under Mod 875, the steel cage was standardised and used until well after the War when, for various reasons, a bronze cage was reintroduced. The Merlin 100 series had a flanged bearing of still higher capacity. One of the problems with investigating this type of failure on service engines was that the damage was always so extensive it was hard to pinpoint the origin and very few bearings were found in trouble at repair.

To improve performance, the central entry supercharger was introduced on the Merlin XX series which were two-speed single-stage engines and the Merlin 40 and 50 series which were single-speed single-stage engines for Spitfire/Seafire operation. The central entry supercharger had a separate entry elbow and this gave rise to some tail end bearing seizures until tooling for reaming the bearing location in the elbow was sorted out so that accurate alignment was achieved [**19**].

The Merlin 46, which had the best altitude performance of any of these engines, was the first to use the true circular arc rotating guide vane having an overhung leading edge and an awkward re-entrant where the leading edge blended into the hub.

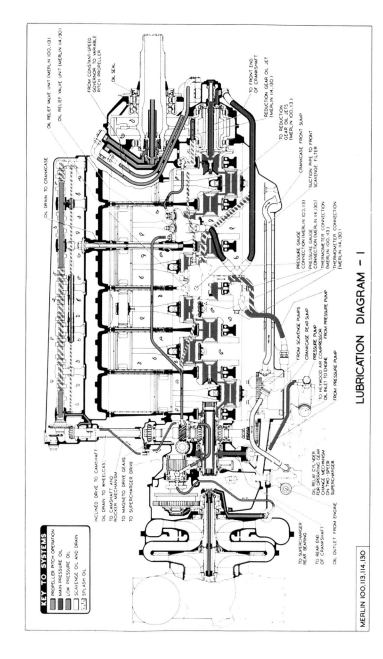

KEY TO SYSTEMS

- PROPELLER PITCH OPERATION
- MAIN PRESSURE OIL
- LOW PRESSURE OIL
- SCAVENGE OIL AND DRAIN
- SPLASH OIL

INCLINED DRIVE TO CAMSHAFT

OIL DRAIN TO WHEELCASE

TO CAMSHAFT AND ROCKER MECHANISM

TO MAGNETO DRIVE GEARS

TO SUPERCHARGER DRIVE

OIL DRAIN TO CRANKCASE

OIL RELIEF VALVE UNIT (MERLIN 100, 113)

OIL RELIEF VALVE UNIT (MERLIN 114, 130)

FROM CONSTANT-SPEED GOVERNOR TO VARIABLE PITCH PROPELLER

OIL SEAL

TO FRONT END OF CRANKSHAFT

REDUCTION GEAR OIL JET (MERLIN 114, 130)

TO REDUCTION GEAR OIL JETS (MERLIN 100, 113)

CRANKCASE FRONT SUMP

SUCTION PIPE TO FRONT SCAVENGE FILTER

PRESSURE GAUGE CONNECTION (MERLIN 100, 113)

PRESSURE GAUGE CONNECTION (MERLIN 114, 130)

THERMOMETER CONNECTION (MERLIN 100, 113)

THERMOMETER CONNECTION (MERLIN 114, 130)

FROM SCAVENGE PUMPS

CRANKCASE REAR SUMP

PRESSURE PUMP

FROM PRESSURE PUMP

TO HEYWOOD AIR COMPRESSOR

OIL INLET TO ENGINE

FROM PRESSURE PUMP

OIL RELAY CYL-KER FOR OPERATING GEAR CHANGE MECHANISM ON TWO-SPEED SUPERCHARGER

TO SUPERCHARGER REAR BEARING

TO REAR END OF CRANKSHAFT

OIL OUTLET FROM ENGINE

LUBRICATION DIAGRAM – I

MERLIN 100, 113, 114, 130

18 End-feed lubrication system

43

It was necessary to ensure that all finish marks ran along the length of the vane and that there were no transverse marks in the root radius while the re-entrant had to be carefully formed. It was essential on rotating guide vane units to maintain a minimum of .002 in conical tip nip to stop vane flutter [20].

The two stage engine appeared in three forms. Engines such as the Merlin 61 and 63 had SU carburettors and the supercharger tail end bearing in the intake elbow.

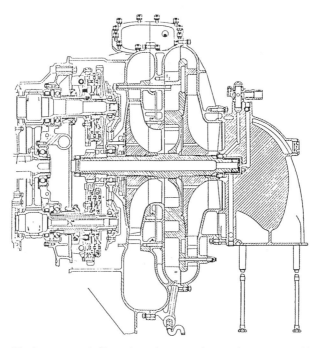

21 Arrangement of two-stage, two-speed supercharger assembly

The Merlin 66 with the Bendix carburettor had a somewhat different arrangement, the tail bearing being carried in a spider in the rear half casing. This gave no trouble in service apart from one operation during the Battle of the Bulge around Christmas 1944. A number of Spitfire IXFs were used for top cover on a Fortress operation. The day turned out to be one of exceptionally low temperatures at altitude and a number of tail bearing seizures occurred on the Merlin 66s which could only be attributed to oil congealing in the transfer feed in the spider, whereas the SU carburettor engines in HF aircraft had an oil hot-spot around the tail bearing and they gave no trouble. Towards the end of the War, the Merlin 100 series engines appeared in Mosquitoes, particularly on PR work. These engines featured a redesigned ball and roller bearing supercharger with an overhung first stage impeller.

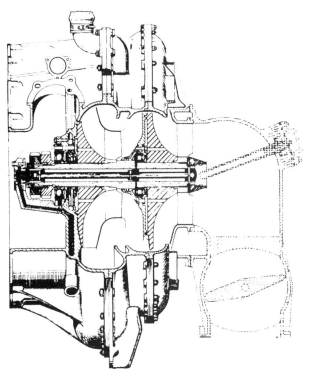

22 Merlin 100 series supercharger, overhung first stage impeller

The Merlin started the War with an SU carburettor [**65**]. It was simple, the mixture being controlled by two needles and a piston-type acceleration pump to handle fuel demands on rapid throttle opening. One needle was operated by a capsule subject to atmosphere and provided the basic fuel requirement and altitude control for the engine. The other was controlled by boost pressure and provided enrichment to stop high power detonation. As the War progressed, lean mixture power was progressively raised to 7 lb boost. With oil heated throttles and water jacketed chokes icing did not occur. The only major operational problem with the carburettor was a rich fluff or hesitation under negative g which received a lot of publicity following the Battle of Britain. It was clear that the fuel injected Daimler Benz engine in the Me 109 had an advantage in entering a dive. The nose of a 109 could be stuffed down without the engine cutting whereas the Merlin fluffed due to an over rich mixture. Tactically the situation was met by the technique of entering a dive off one wingtip. A negative g carburettor was developed and two squadrons on Spitfire VIs at North Weald were so equipped. However, this carburettor could not sense zero g and was not operationally successful. The situation was partially improved by the introduction of the RAE restrictor in the main fuel line which limited the amount of excess fuel that could be delivered to the engine at full throttle. However, Rolls-Royce and RAE developments produced an anti g carburettor with different valving on the float chamber, to resist the effects of both negative and positive g. These carburettors were used in all later SU applications including the two stage engines. There was also embodiment of the necessary modifications during repair. (See Appendix VI)

The Merlin 66 and its high altitude 70 Series counterparts were fitted with a Rolls-Royce development of the American Bendix injection carburettor which sprayed fuel into the eye of the supercharger at about 5 lb per square inch pressure and did not suffer g effects. It did however have some problems of its own. If air entered the metering control chambers, its de-aerating properties were such that it could not clear the airlock and a complete engine cut would occur. This could arise on Spitfire operations where droptanks were being carried. If, as was the practice with SU carburettored aircraft, the engine was allowed to run out of fuel on droptanks before jettisoning to give maximum range, it was very difficult to get a Merlin 66 restarted. The trouble was finally fixed by venting the 'D' metering chamber and fitting a vane-type petrol pump, instead of the Rolls-Royce gear variety, which would pump a much greater head of air and clear the carburettor.

The Merlin 100 Series went over to fuel injection with a single point SU injection pump with the nozzle in the eye of the supercharger. In his 1945 Merlin paper,* Cyril Lovesey indicates that the latent heat effect of the evaporation of fuel in the blower improved the compression ratio by about 7 per cent compared with inlet port injection.

---

* *Development of the Rolls-Royce Merlin from 1939 to 1945* by A C Lovesey, published in Aircraft Engineering, July 1946.

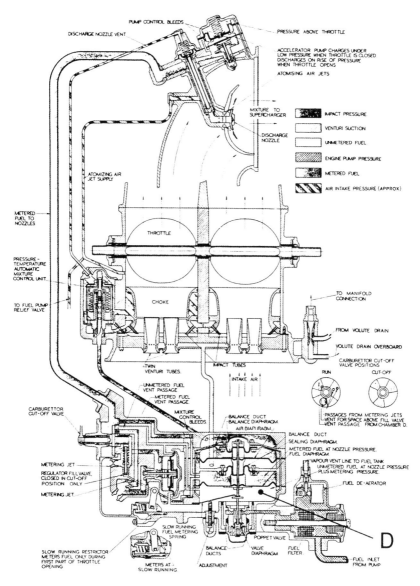

23 RR Bendix injection carburettor. The 'D' chamber was vented to prevent aeration problems

Such a system required a more complex fuel metering pump and individual injectors. A side issue was the pipe runs involved. Experience on the Merlin, with its long propeller oil feed pipes, had shown that rigid steel construction was not the epitome of reliability and to overcome this problem the Company had adopted Weatherhead hose in such applications. The construction of the high pressure hose consisted of a rubber inner sleeve surrounded by flexible steel braiding which in turn was protected by a rubber outer sleeve. Although somewhat bulky it proved to be very reliable and eliminated the problems of steel pipes.

However, even with the advantages conferred by this design, the runs would not have been very convenient and the system would have added a large number of additional fuel connections in the engine bay.

The liquid cooled intercoolers gave little trouble apart from a few failures of soldering on early matrices which was cured by using a softer 50/50 solder.

The charge temperature on the Merlin 61 was about 205°C at the entry to the intercooler and in practice it was found that about 40 per cent intercooling gave the best results. This allowed a suitable reduction in charge temperature while at the same time retaining a small enough intercooler radiator to minimise drag. Percentage intercooling as expressed above is a measure of the reduction in charge temperature across the intercooler.

Supercharger drive

The supercharger drive was installed at the back of the wheelcase with a spring driveshaft running through the central hollow drive carrying the main auxiliary drive bevel gear.

The primary drive was a gear engaging with three layshafts with three large gears mating with the pinion or pinions on the supercharger rotor shaft.

On single speed engines, there was a bronze pad slipper drive in the layshaft gear to provide a smooth take-up of sudden changes in crankshaft speed. This assembly gave no trouble.

The two speed supercharger drive was of the Farman type with multi plate friction clutches to transfer the drive from the layshaft to the final drive gears. The loading on the clutches was obtained by bob weights on the withdrawal fingers to provide centrifugal load on the clutch in the engaged position [25].

The upper layshaft was the moderate speed (MS) ratio while the lower two provided the full speed (FS) ratio. Engagement of either gear was effected by a camshaft operated by a two position valve whose servo was scavenge oil pressure. The cams controlled operating levers with withdrawal races allowing MS or FS to be engaged, the gear not required having its clutch disengaged by the withdrawal race pushing

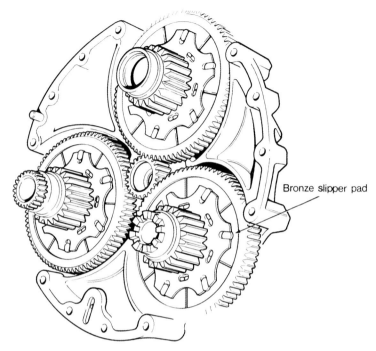

Bronze slipper pad

24 Single speed supercharger drive

in the fingers on the bob weights and removing the load from the clutch.

The Merlin X gave no trouble but as production of higher rated engines from new factories increased so did the problems. Clutch reliability was finally obtained by detail action in a number of areas. First the timing of the operation was important to ensure that there was a clean change. With multi-plate clutches the amount of free movement in the disengaged position had to be controlled to about 0.030 in. With less end float the clutches tended to drag when not in use and overheat, and if there was too much end float the geometry was such that in the loaded condition the fingers could contact the withdrawal race causing clutch slip and burn out.

The issues turned on getting good solid clutches with adequate friction plate bedding. In rivetting the linings to the plates one could get a series of waves and high spots which wore rapidly and increased end float. This was cured by attention to the backing plates for flatness, care in rivetting and final grinding of friction surfaces.

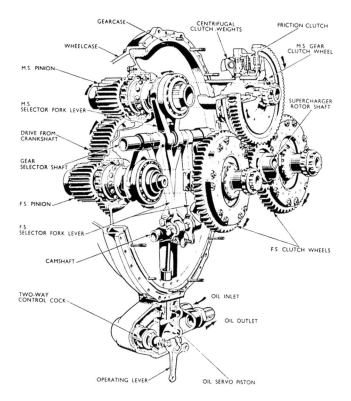

25 Supercharger gear change mechanism

The steel driven plates were built up in two halves for lightness and rivetted together and tended to be 'spongy'. This was finally cured by a production simplification scheme for solid steel ground plates.

A further refinement as a result of operating experience in the Far East was to treat the driving plates with a corrosion inhibitor prior to fitting the linings. Certain linings proved to be hygroscopic which could cause a build up of corrosion between the lining and plate, dangerously reducing end float in the pack.

On some aircraft the operation of the changeover valve was mechanical and a spring toggle was introduced on the valve to prevent aircraft wing movement 'niggling' at the valve and causing clutch slip.

The MS pack on early engines had an umbrella gear to drive the supercharger pinion. It was an awkward looking design with the teeth overhung from the web. Mod 411 improved the shape of the web in an attempt to introduce some flexibility, but it was not made reliable until the gear was redesigned with a central web as part of the clutch pack. (Mod 659).

Wheelcase

This casing which bolted on to the back of the crankcase provided all the drives necessary to the engine. It contained the main drive to the supercharger gears with an inner torsion shaft. On the solid outer member was the main bevel driving the upper and lower vertical drives. The upper vertical drive carried a bronze skew gear which drove the magnetos via a horizontal steel gear carried on bearings in the casing. At its top end was a bevel driving the two lower inclined bevels which transmitted power to the camshaft bevels in the cylinder heads via spline drive shafts. These also provided a vernier effect for valve timing. The lower vertical shaft drove the fuel pump via an aluminium skew gear and the coolant pump by a quill shaft from its lower extremity. The oil pump stack in the lower half of the crankcase was driven by a spur train with its driving gear on the shaft.

Grinding of bevel gears had not then arrived so the gears were cut and hardened. Care had to be taken to minimise heat treatment distortions but bedding was always a problem. The teeth were cut with mitred faces to provide a basic setting for backlash.

Even so, with local tooth variations and the somewhat lively drive, tooth scuffing and plucking were often present, but the gears kept working and gave little trouble. The besetting problem was the bronze magneto skew gear which occasionally failed, losing the drive to both magnetos, when as one pilot said drily, 'things went bloody quiet'.

At repair one would find perfect gears, plucked gears, and gears with savage cutting in at the roots caused by the driven steel gear. There was never a lead, John Maddocks (*Mx*) and Freddie Allwood (*Ald*) spent a lot of time on the problem. Every aspect, including tooth form, finish and tip radius on the gears and lubrication by means of an oil bath, was followed up but which no real success. Flexible couplings were introduced in the magneto drive shafts but the odd failure still occurred, and then the heavens fell in. In the Summer of 1942 Alex Henshaw, Chief Test Pilot of the Castle Bromwich Spitfire Factory, had a series of failures in quick succession. Henshaw naturally rang *Hs* and as a result *By* took charge of the issue personally.

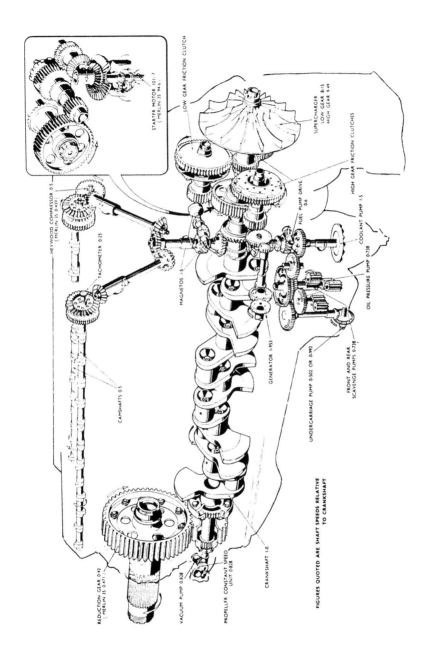

LOW GEAR FRICTION CLUTCH

STARTER MOTOR 101·7 (MERLIN JS 94·6)

SUPERCHARGER LOW GEAR 8·15 HIGH GEAR 9·49

HIGH GEAR FRICTION CLUTCHES

HEYWOOD COMPRESSOR 0·5 (MERLIN JS 0·479)

FUEL PUMP DRIVE 0·6

COOLANT PUMP 1·5

TACHOMETER 0·25

MAGNETOS 1·5

OIL PRESSURE PUMP 0·738

CAMSHAFTS 0·5

GENERATOR 1·953

UNDERCARRIAGE PUMP 0·502 OR 0·992

FRONT AND REAR SCAVENGE PUMPS 0·738

FIGURES QUOTED ARE SHAFT SPEEDS RELATIVE TO CRANKSHAFT

REDUCTION GEAR 0·42 (MERLIN JS 0·477)

VACUUM PUMP 0·828

PROPELLER CONSTANT SPEED UNIT 0·828

CRANKSHAFT 1·0

26 Typical gear trains

52

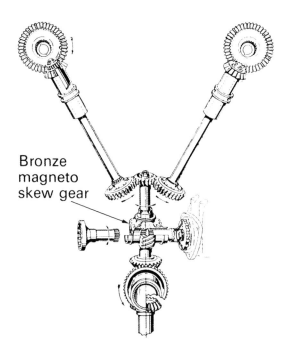

Bronze
magneto
skew gear

27 Valve and magneto timing gear

Having a number of engines to examine helped in the detail analysis. It began to appear that there was a relationship between the backlash in the main drive bevels and the backlash in the skew gears, but this did not tie up completely. A failed engine with only a new skew gear fitted was tested with what for the time was a lot of instrumentation. To cut the story short, it was found that on some engines the crankshaft was shuttling rearwards with considerable force, to the extent that it distorted the centre bearing panel in the crankcase by .010 to .012 in. On the Merlin the crankshaft was located by flanges on the centre bearing and it was the load on the flange that was distorting the centre bearing panel, which in turn meant that, with the friction in the splines, there was end load in the wheelcase that was pushing the main drive bevel out of mesh with the mating gear on the upper vertical drive. Thus, due to the wide clearances on the driving bevels, the skew gear was exposed to the heavy loads generated by the torsionals present and in consequence failed. On engines where the main drive bevels maintained their clearances, they protected the skew gears.

It was clear that if engines could be built so that the main drive bevels had half the backlash of the skew gears and this could be maintained under running conditions, the skew gear failures would be overcome. The remaining problem was the end movement of the crankshaft and how it could be prevented. Further testing proved that the end load was generated by the interaction of the loose spline coupling between the reduction gear pinion and the crankshaft, the loading from the splines forcing the crank rearwards. More experiments during engine running showed that this was caused by slight malalignment between the splines in the crankshaft and the splines in the front of the reduction gear pinion, when the front of the pinion was low in relation to the rear locating pinion bore in the crankcase. It was found quite empirically, that by raising the front of the pinion so that its locating bore was .0015 in above the rear bore, the whole assembly was stabilised. The splined coupling tended to draw the crankshaft forward so that it was located normally by the rear thrust face on the centre main bearing. Engines built this way were shown to maintain the desired backlashes in the main drive bevels and skew gears. The formal instruction was Technical Instruction Sheet number BY.70 and after its implementation no further skew gear failures occurred. The principle was known as 'co-related backlash'.

Alex Henshaw refers to this series of failures and his consequent narrow escapes in his book '*Sigh for a Merlin*' and I think he is very forbearing.

While on the subject of test flying it was inevitable that test pilots would have more engine troubles than squadron pilots. In experimental and development test flying new engine types and higher and higher ratings were being explored and in consequence failures occurred. Production test pilots flew large numbers of aircraft and experienced engine faults for the following reasons:

1. The random engine with some defect which, particularly in the learner phases and in spite of the care taken, got through test and inspection procedures undetected and then failed shortly afterwards.

2. A new engine or modification coming on to production and giving some unexpected trouble. An example was the Mod 656 piston which deleted the top scraper ring. This gave rise to a number of short life piston seizures. Inspection of pistons after endurance test was called up but a few failures occurred on production flying until improved skirt lubrication (Mod 742) cured the problem.

3. The epidemic peculiar to a batch of engines and without obvious cause, eg the

bronze magneto skew gear.

4. Sparking plug failures or defects in the aircraft oil or cooling systems which manifested themselves to the pilot as a major engine failure.

These hazards were appreciated and continual efforts were made not only to avoid them, but to react effectively when troubles arose.

Beside the skew gear episode defects were fairly random but there were a few failures of the upper vertical drive shaft. The assembly of the shaft depended upon distance pieces between the nut securing the bronze skew gear and the upper vertical bevel. The skew gear was keyed to the shaft and failures occurred at the root of the keyway and in the bore of the shaft at its top end. It was evident that the shaft was being distorted by lack of squareness in the assembly. At the same time trouble was experienced with the nut securing the upper vertical bevel to the shaft.

The shaft was modified by locating the skew gear with cross pins and the top bevel was located on a shoulder on the shaft. The retaining nut fitted on a taper collet located in the gear and a vernier tab washer was provided to make the locking of the nut easier. These changes simplified production and effected the cure.

The lower inclined drive bevels, in the top of the wheelcase, were each located by two ball bearings. Both bearings on each sub assembly were retained by a single nut. This rendered it most difficult to ensure that both bearings were locked and if this was not done correctly, failure of the bearings occurred. The trouble was cured by making two separate nuts which simplified build and ensured that the bearings were correctly locked.

Cylinder blocks

The single piece block which carried the brunt of early operations used the liner flange and spigot to make a gas and coolant seal at the combustion chamber, the bottom flange of the liners being located on the crankcase [**3, 4**]. The cylinder studs therefore made both the coolant and gas seal, as well as carrying the firing loads, assisted by clamps on either side of the liner engaging with the underside of the flange. Thus the cylinder liners felt not only combustion pressures but also the dynamic distortions of the crankcase. Progressive improvements were made to the design which included the fully shrouded joint ring to Mod 155 to get away from partial shrouding which had previously existed where two liners were adjacent to each other. External coolant leaks at the base of the cylinder block were overcome by Mod 231 which provided a triple seal ring instead of a single bootlace seal.

A picture tends to be painted of single piece block engines with top joints leaking like colanders and being a risk to the pilots. In fact most engines did not have blocks changed for leaks in the course of a normal life and when engines were pulled for leaks, their total was not the major cause of engine removals, although probably in the top five. The leaks tended to be more prevalent in fighter operations where engines were subjected to constantly changing conditions. Early Mosquitoes suffered also, but this was traced to overheating caused by long periods of taxying, the aircraft having leading edge radiators. Improved ground handling techniques overcame the problem.

The two piece block enabled the boost potential of the Merlin to be exploited and life to be extended. It was designed with a dry top joint, the liner being trapped between head and skirt, there being no contact between gas and coolant. The gas joint was made by the side studs between the head and skirt as well as the main cylinder holding down studs, made in chrome vanadium steel, which also took the firing loads. The liners had no compressive loads, these being taken by the aluminium block assembly, the high thermal expansion of aluminium requiring flexible stud material [28].

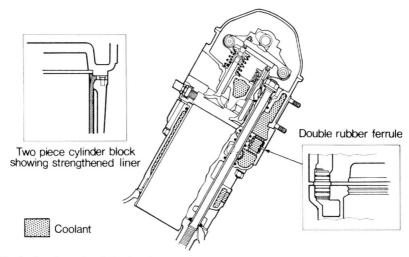

Two piece cylinder block showing strengthened liner

Double rubber ferrule

Coolant

28 Section through cylinder head

Two piece blocks were subsequently fitted to the Merlin XX without changing the nickel steel studs but reducing their torque loading.

Coolant flow between head and skirt was effected by transfer ferrules with rubber ring seals at each end. These did give some leakage problems externally but were cured by the use of double rubber ferrules. A few stud tube rubber seal leaks occurred which would allow coolant to leak into the crankcase. These were overcome by employment of the straight sided vee groove, which became a Rolls-Royce standard in such applications, and by getting ring to groove volume ratios right.

The two piece block did not instantly kill off the internal leak; some liners failed in fatigue at the flange radius, cracking locally through to the cylinder bore. This was cured by Mod 674, which was an early example of a taper fillet radius to reduce the stress between the flange and cylinder.

The skirt also tended to crack on the exhaust side at two and five cylinders adjacent to the side stud bosses. This was overcome by Mod 700 which embodied a strengthening rib along the skirt. At repair, it was possible to weld in a rib at two and five locations on existing skirts, a comment on the advance of repair techniques using aluminium welding.

The following items on the cylinder block are of interest:

Valve Springs

Over a long period Rolls-Royce had developed valve springs in chrome vanadium wire, drawn to a special technique, coiled and then hardened and tempered.

Inlet and exhaust valve springs were identical with inner and outer members. They were very reliable but when the odd failure occurred it was almost always on the inlet side. Failures could be traced to intermittent inclusions on the wire, which were very difficult to trace, or to corrosion pits. Shot peening overcame the effects of inclusions and the corrosion pits just stopped by stove-enamelling the springs.

Inlet Valves

A number of valve failures occurred in early operations. These included fractures of the tulip and at the collet location. The tulip failures were cured by stiffening the rim of the valve. The collet location failures taught us a very hard lesson. At that time .020 in tappet clearance as a cold setting applied to both inlet and exhaust valves, it being thought that both clearances closed up with temperature. This was true on the exhaust valve but the opposite occurred on the inlet, the clearance rising and causing valve fracture occasionally.

The inlet valve clearance was reduced to .010 in with instructions for field embodiment. Sufficient judgement was not given to this decision. With 24 inlet valves per engine and thousands of engines and human error in resetting tappets, the results were far worse than sweating it out until routine checks. Numerous failures occurred due to incorrect clearances. The worst case was where a tappet nut on an engine in a Halifax was left loose causing an inlet valve failure. On this occasion it led to torching into the induction system, an engine fire that could not be put out and burned until the outboard wing section fell away. The aircraft crashed with the loss of 11 lives on a special flight.

Valves would also occasionally fail from frettage fatigue at the collet location. Phosphor bronze collets were introduced and proved effective, replacing steel in this application.

Exhaust Valves

The standard valves were made in KE 965 with sodium cooled stems and gave little trouble at military lives but a few casualties were occurring at 420 hrs. Various seating combinations were tried, but in wartime, Brightray on the valve seat and Stellite on the seat in the head gave as good results as any. On transport engines lengthened close clearance valve guides to provide better valve control and locked bottom washers to promote valve rotation gave a life of 500 hrs reliably.

Valve Rockers

Rocker pads were a problem which responded to increasing the depth of hard chromium on the rocker pad face. This was increased from a minimum of .003 to .006 in and later to .012 in thickness. However great care had to be taken to maintain the correct form on the steel surface and to ensure that surface preparation and plating control were of a high order. When grinding the final form no 'dry striking' of the grinding wheel was permitted as this would crack the plated surface. Operators had tended to feed in the cut with coolant turned off to give them a better view of the work piece.

Camshaft Bracket Studs

A number of stripped threads occurred at the number 7 bracket position, sometimes leading to the failure of the stud which remained secure in the head and ultimately to camshaft failure, generally at the oil holes in the number 7 bracket.

There is no doubt that much of this came from variations in thread quality in the cylinder head and increases in loadings from the aircraft auxiliaries driven from the back of the camshafts. It was necessary in the long term to fit larger studs under Mod 298.

As an aside, when the Merlin was designed it was thought to be a competitive advantage to mount aircraft auxiliaries at various points on the engine, instead of using an auxiliary gearbox with a single engine drive. In practice this was not so, engines had to be dressed with suitable units and an engine change meant breaking and remaking inaccessible connections concerned only with aircraft systems, although this was made a little easier when a complete powerplant was involved. There was also inter-action between units and their engine drives to the debit of both. For example, units mounted on the back of the cylinder heads were driven via a compound spur gear bolted to the cam bevel. In the end it was necessary to have larger fitting bolts and a machined annular spacer under the bolt heads, with improved locking of the nuts, to cope with the loads imposed by the driven units, making it an expensive little assembly.

The units on one engine could be an impressive array. There were mountings for two pumps or compressors at the rear of each cylinder head, an undercarriage pump driven from the lower half and a generator with a drive shaft from the wheelcase but mounted on the side of the engine. At the front, driven by a quill from the reduction gear pinion, was the dual drive which carried a vacuum pump and constant speed unit, the latter of necessity being engine driven. If the aircraft required a cabin blower, the engine used a Coffman starter type crankcase, the blower being mounted on the starter facing and driven from the reduction gear. The lesson was learned on the Griffon, which drove a separate wheelcase for aircraft units and was generally trouble free.

Exhaust Manifold Studs

This may not sound a major issue but it is an example of how a nuisance became a major hazard. There had been a number of exhaust manifold stud failures but these had not caused a lot of trouble. Development had been going on and almost without comment an Austenitic stud in KE 965 was introduced. The logic behind this was that its heat resisting qualities made it better than the standard stud material in this location.

Almost immediately a spate of exhaust stud failures occurred, mostly on Mosquitoes, which allowed exhaust stacks to come adrift, with flame impingement on the power plant and ignition harness, producing a considerable fire risk. *Dor* became involved as the result of a high level rocket from the RAF and asked *By* to go and look at a Hucknall aircraft urgently. It was obvious to *By* that KE 965 had not the strength or ductility needed for a stud. There was ample room to use a longer stud with a reach nut and, properly designed, this could be in the Company's standard 3½% nickel steel stud material. The trouble was aggravated by open copper asbestos gaskets which collapsed with use. The final solution was a lengthened stud with a waisted shank and a reach nut, to be used with a totally enclosed copper asbestos washer and, longer term, a solid copper gasket.

Induction pipes and flame traps

The flame trap modification has been previously mentioned and as a cure for backfiring worked well at the lower power ratings. However, with life, flame trap clogging became a problem and continued to be so off and on throughout the history of the engine.

A coarse mesh flame trap was introduced under Mod 185 but the clogging continued. At that time it was thought that the problem arose from oil leaking past the supercharger tail bearing and flinger ring on the ball race, contaminating the flame traps, as well as occasional leakage from the carburettor spindle seals. It was obvious that some engines had higher supercharger oil consumptions than others and some of this could apparently be attributed to varying groove sizes in the tail bearing bushes. Fuel dye also contributed, as well as dust in the air stream, but it was not consistent.

Some engines clogged traps and some did not. Some operations were worse than others, in particular the Halifax squadrons on the Special Operations Executive (SOE) operations suffered. It was also thought, when a few cracked reduction gear casings occurred on Lancasters, that differential sludging was producing combustion roughness. In general however routine changes of flame traps were the answer and this was done as experience dictated, being less of a nuisance on two piece block engines where set screw located induction pipes enabled flame traps to be changed without lifting a block. Post War, when civil engines had piston ring seals on the supercharger bearings, the trouble was still with us. Cleaning flame traps was a problem. Conventional methods left a residue of deposit which gave rise to rapid choking if flame traps were refitted in this condition. An effective method was a long soak in white spirit which softened the deposits which enabled them to be blown clear with a jet of white spirit or air blast.

More serious, however, was the mechanical failure of flame traps due to normal vibration causing the frames to break down and the foils to come adrift. This led to positive set screw location and the welding into the induction system of blanks which kept groups of three cylinders isolated on each block and stopped a backfire from running the length of the open inlet port in the block. It became evident on highly boosted engines that the flame traps could not deal with a really heavy backfire arising from pre-ignition. A number of spectacular blow backs occurred on early 25 lb boost operations due to maintenance problems with sparking plugs. In the end result these were overcome when using Lodge RS5/5 plugs with solid copper washers and correctly torqued.

Cooling systems

Early Merlins used 100 per cent ethylene glycol cooling which allowed 135° coolant temperature, but with the advent of the Merlin XII a major move was made to pressure water cooling using 30 per cent glycol as anti-freeze. The advantages of water as a cooling medium are considerable. With 135°C coolant temperature the mixture at 15 lb per square inch reduces the cylinder head metal temperature by some 30°C when compared with 100 per cent glycol.

The introduction of pressure cooling had some side effects. The Merlin had always used Parkerised mild steel coolant pipes but as soon as pressure cooling came in corrosion failures of the pipes occurred. Very small quantities of sulphuric acid were found in the cooling systems and while it was at first thought to be sabotage, it turned out to be no more sinister than coolant being drained into carboys as a convenient container, but retaining an acid residue. In a number of squadrons the bulk coolant supply thus became contaminated. The cure was to fit brass or Tungum coolant pipes but it did alert us quickly to the deterioration of glycol water mixtures and the rapid corrosion effects at electrolytic couples, formed by the junction of dissimilar metals. This led to the introduction of inhibited coolants and regular testing to control acidity.

Soon after pressure cooled engines came on to production they began to show overheated cylinder blocks. This was traced to small amounts of oil in coolant passages left from manufacturing operations. Glycol would dissolve it but not water and the oil formed a film which cut down heat transfer. Sodium metasilicate wash of cooling systems overcame this but even ½ per cent of oil was sufficient to do damage and as a result the Company was always suspicious of oil inhibited coolants.

The first Merlin coolant pumps had a typical packing gland which was never satisfactory because, apart from anything else, they were always over-tightened in service and would burn the pump spindle. The thrust of the rotor was borne on a thrust button on the rotor which used to wear also.

As the War progressed Morganite bearings were introduced and the final standard

61

was a ball bearing coolant pump with a packless gland running on a Morganite ring.

The Mosquito differed from other installations in that it had a reverse flow system pumping through the radiator instead of drawing from it. In practice it was no different from conventional flow systems.

Propeller reduction gears

Whereas the Kestrel had offered a number of reduction gear ratios and was designed with a completely detachable gear unit in its own casings, the Merlin started life with .477:1 only. Neither was it designed with a separate gear unit, the rear half casing being formed by the crankcase, but as the gear assembly was housed in the front casing it was still easy to change reduction gears. When the Merlin was being considered for a heavy bomber, a .42:1 ratio was chosen because a bomber could swing a bigger propeller giving more take-off thrust. This was important with the less favourable power to weight ratio of the aircraft. However, the .42 gear became the most commonly used ratio on both fighters and bombers and only the Spitfire engines retained the .477 ratio with the exception of the Merlin 61.

Single stage Packard engines for the RAF used the .42 ratio but all other Packard built engines employed a .479 ratio. Presumably the slight variation from the higher ratio Merlin was in the interests of manufacture. Post War the Merlin 140 with its contra-rotating gear had a .512 ratio. It will be noted that early Merlins had a parallel diameter propeller shaft but a shaft with a neck-down front section was soon adopted (Merlin III). This was to allow a smaller diameter propeller retaining nut to be used and thus avoid damage to the threads on the shaft when the propeller was being fitted.

The gear loadings involved called for great accuracy in manufacture and Rolls-Royce pioneered the use of form grinding Orcutt machines which enabled involute tip correction to be applied. This was necessary to compensate for the dynamic deflections in the reduction gear pinion which resulted in early engagement of the following tooth. Tip correction thus avoided tooth scuffing and breakdown which would otherwise have occurred. Form grinding was developed because on contemporary machines, which generated gear profiles, it was only possible to correct by barrelling the tooth and departing from the involute form.

Both tip and root corrections were used as power ratings increased and today on turboprop engines are even more essential than on the Merlin. When tip corrections were introduced the amount was judged by examining bedding patterns after engine test and, while today more advanced methods are used to determine correction factors, the experienced eye is as good a guide as any.

On the Merlin gear the drive from the crank to the pinion was by a loose coupling engaging with splines in the front of the pinion bore. Because of this it was necessary to set the pinion with the initial bedding at the rear of the teeth. Thus as the load increased an even bedding pattern was achieved over the length of the tooth. If these conditions were not complied with, 'window paning' would occur which would eventually cause tooth breakdown.

Quite early in the War, some pinion tooth failures occurred due to the hard case having been ground out of the tooth root spaces. It was then found that the Rockwell Hardness Tester could not get into the root space, a simple lesson but a real one, cured by slimming the probe on the machine. As production increased the precision gear manufacturing task, which included the gears in the supercharger drive train, outstripped tooth profile measuring capacity. The only manufacturer of suitable inspection machines was Maag who were then isolated from Britain. *By* set to and designed a suitable machine in-house, getting the pantographs made by the Venner Time Switch Company, so that a graph of every ground gear could be retained in inspection records. Unless the grinding process was carefully controlled, grinding abuse could occur including softening and rehardening as well as grinding cracks. The main causes were dry striking of the wheel and inadequate trimming which caused the grinding wheel to become 'loaded' by fine metallic particles produced in metal removal. Whitehead (*EJW*), one of the Company's very senior metallurgists developed the electrolytic sulphuric acid and nitric acid etching of gears to detect these faults and enable manufacture to be better controlled. These have become standard methods of gear and bearing track inspection in the Company and emphasise the concentration on quality control as well as output in the War years.

Mention has been made of aircraft and propeller vibrations affecting reduction gear reliability. These led to some cases of cracking of reduction gear casings at propeller shaft and pinion bores, but the majority of trouble lay in the various bearings and their locations.

The pinion bearings were located in steel housings shrunk into the crankcase and reduction gear cover bores. The rear propeller shaft bearing was similarly located, while the front roller bearing fitted in the housing for the ball thrust bearing. Vibrations on both Halifax and Mosquito caused, first, spinning of the roller bearings in their housings and subsequently movement of the steel housings in their casings. The resulting wear was such that the gears would get out of line and fail due to plucking and overload. This was tackled by chromium plating the housing bores to stop them wearing and by increasing the fit of the housings in their casings to around .006 in diametral nip.

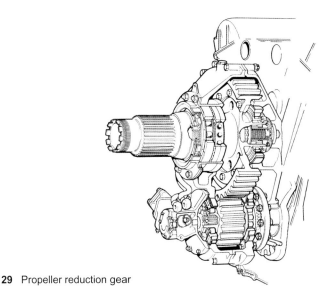

29 Propeller reduction gear

In the Mosquito the worst trouble was violent spinning of the outer track of the rear propshaft bearing in its housing, to the extent that it wore away its keep plates and came forward out of its housing. This was cured by replacing keep plates with a continuous retaining ring with a hardened face. Finally the bore of the thrust bearing housing was chromium plated to prevent the front roller bearing outer race from wearing its location, while the diameter for the inner track on the propeller shaft was chromed to maintain the bearing fit. The bronze nut which clamped the inner race axially did not prevent the bearing from spinning.

It was decided to live with the Halifax situation and to rework engines at repair to embody the various modifications. In the squadrons four bladed propellers were fitted as supplies allowed. The demands of the Pathfinder Mosquito force were such that working parties fitted new bearing housings in the field, using liquid oxygen to enable assembly of the high interference housings and embodying the continuous retaining ring, changes which gave a satisfactory standard of reliability.

The reduction gear wheel was secured to the propeller shaft by fitted taper bolts and as the War progressed some failures occurred. The bolt holes in the gear and shaft were taper reamed to give about .030 in draw. Examination of the failures indicated that the bolt heads had not been seating when the retaining nuts had been tightened. Instructions were issued to ensure that the degree of draw was not exceeded and that the bolt heads were tapped home and feeler gauge checked for seating before being tightened. As a further precaution the chambering in the bolts was deleted to make them solid. These modifications did not completely cure the problem which was undoubtedly aggravated by aircraft vibration, and the ultimate solution was to double the number of bolts.

Connectings rods and pistons

The connecting rod assembly followed Rolls-Royce practice having a curved foot marine type fork rod, with a blade rod running on the outer diameter of the fork rod bearing block. Early Merlins had a solid big end with lead bronze cast on to the inner and outer diameter of the block, the bore of the blade rod running directly on the lead bronze surface. Lubrication was by four oil holes drilled through the block. Loose shell bearings were then introduced using 2 per cent tin lead bronze on the fork rod bearing and 8 per cent tin lead bronze on the blade rod, the shells fitting conventionally in the blade rod bore. The lubrication holes were retained but there was also a continuous lubrication groove in the rather narrow blade rod bearing. The lapping motion of the blade rod with its hard bearing material tended to wear the carbon steel track, producing quite severe stepping at the groove, particularly in desert operations. This was much improved by deleting the groove in the blade rod bearing and putting a very narrow oil groove in the fork rod shell.

Two lessons were learned as the result of the change to loose shell bearings. The first was the need to hold .001 to .002 in diametral nip on the bearing shells, otherwise they would spin and fail. This led to the technique of measuring circumferential length and bearing section to control bearing sizes and was also applied to main bearings. The second lesson was that with either the Rolls-Royce sheared tang or Allison crushed tang location, the positioning of the shells in their respective halves of the connecting rods during assembly was essential, otherwise the tang could be trapped, causing the bearing shells to be dragged round with subsequent failure. The gudgeon pin bush was made in a high quality phosphor bronze and had to be precise fit in the eye of the connecting rod so that it did not creep. It was not therefore a floating bush, all movement taking place between the bore of the bush and the gudgeon pin. If the correct fit was not maintained the bush could creep and wear, causing the rod to fail at the little end. Post War, the bush was made in LT10, a high tin lead bronze.

Connecting rods were made in 5 per cent nickel steel and one reason for the choice of this material was its tolerance in the forging process, whereas nickel chrome steel could easily 'burn'. With a marine type rod the control of the radius in the arch of the fork rod and the mating face on the bearing block was very important. There had to be a very slight gap at the apex of the arch to ensure good bedding around the bolt holes. If the arch on the bearing block was bearing on the apex of the connecting rod arch then severe fretting would occur around the boltholes, leading to fatigue failure from fretting and pluck marks. Correctly controlled, no problems arose.

The fork rod would occasionally fail in fatigue from the inner corner of the bolt head trap and a good radius was necessary along the edge of the trap, which had to run smoothly through the 90° corner involved. To cope with increasing boost pressures strengthened connecting rods were introduced under Merlin Mod 399.

Unhappily the original design of bolt location was retained but with deeper section in the arch. These rods looked wrong and were wrong, failing more frequently at this point than the original rod. A further change was necessary to introduce the elegant blended radius rod to Mod 587 which got rid of the bolt trap and not only looked right but was absolutely reliable.

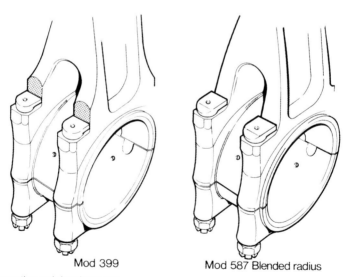

Mod 399   Mod 587 Blended radius

30 Connecting rod development

Because Packard were less flexible in embodiment of modification, engines from this source used the Mod 399 rod for much longer and ran into a number of characteristic failures. When examined the Packard rods appeared to be well finished with heavy polishing of the radius and associated areas. British experience was that rods free from finishing scores were far less prone to failure and this apparent contradiction was surprising. However, when the rods were etched it was found that the polishing operation had swaged material into deep score marks, masking them from visual inspection, and failures could therefore be expected. It was a lesson in the effect of heavy over-polishing.

The connecting rod bolts were made in 3½ per cent nickel steel with a Brinell range of 248 to 272. Being a ductile material the technique was to tighten the bolts until plastic deformation occurred, ensuring maximum tension. This could be done either using a torque spanner or by a very simple technique of nipping up the assembly and then tightening to the next castellation on the nut. Practical experience showed that in an overspeed the bolts would begin to stretch at above 4,500 rpm, effectively 1,000 rpm above the terminal velocity limit. The nuts were split-pinned using close fitting centreless ground Staybrite pins. Split pins made to normal aero standard would fail in fatigue and fall out.

The Merlin was not subject to failures caused by hydraulic locking in the cylinders but on occasion very severe overpriming prior to start up could cause locking in end cylinders, with consequent failure, but such instances were a rarity.

Four basic types of piston, of which there were a number of variants, were used during the War. They were all made from RR 56 forgings. The first piston had three gas rings with two scraper rings and an extended skirt below the bottom scraper. The second type was generally similar but had a deep top land and two gas rings. Both pistons suffered from fatigue failures of the skirt at the lower scraper groove. This never caused any trouble, except that some engines were rejected for bits of skirt in the filters. The trouble was thought to be due to internal stress and a boiling water quench was introduced during manufacture. This did not cure the trouble and Cyril Lovesey (*Lov*) in his pragmatic way, decided that the engine did not mind skirtless pistons, so that was the way they should be made. When the Merlin 66 was introduced it had the first double girder piston, with three narrow gas rings, two scraper rings and no skirt below the bottom scraper. In terms of bedding and general operation it was the best piston so far seen. However, at high boost/low rpm cruise the narrow gas rings, being light, tended to gum. To avoid this a new piston had to be designed with three standard gas rings, which entailed deleting the top scraper and its oil drain holes. The inertia of the standard gas rings kept them from gumming at low rpm. When introduced on production there was an immediate spate of piston seizures. It was then found that the top scraper, and oil drain holes, had been lubricating the skirt. Re-instating the drain holes was an effective cure.

A number of piston failures were induced by gas ring fractures, which would allow pieces of ring to hammer their way through the lands, when torching could occur, with piston burning. A change in ring material from 4K6 to DTD485, which was like steel, together with close control of toe out limits on the ring ends stopped the breakages.

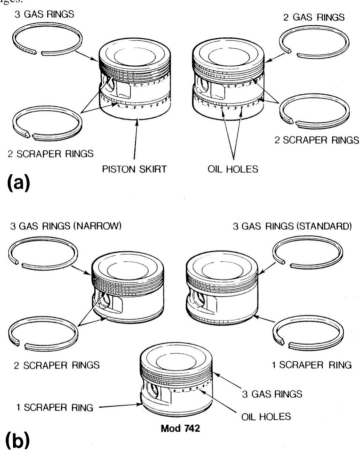

31 Merlin piston development
    [a] skirted
    [b] un-skirted

Scraper ring failures were very few and generally occurred in the top ring position and were thought to be due to carbon packing behind the ring. This was cured by the deletion of the top scraper. The bottom scraper did not suffer in this way but there were a few ring failures due to fatigue cracking at the oil holes. These were apparently caused by the use of blunt drills during manufacture and appropriate action fixed the problem. The other source of piston failure was pre-ignition caused by defective or loose sparking plugs. An overheated plug causing pre-ignition at high powers would burn a hole in a piston crown in seconds, with consequent torching and blow piping that would rapidly destroy the piston.

One sideline in piston development which indicates how increased duty affected relatively minor components concerned the gudgeon pin circlip. This had been a comparatively light ring with a stop screw to prevent the circlip from rotating. As powers went up there were both circlip failures and stop screws coming adrift. This was fixed by getting rid of the stop screws and fitting a massive circlip made out of .080 in diameter wire with an accurately controlled form to stop the ends of the circlip vibrating and breaking up.

Some associated problems

What has been said so far has dealt largely with RAF operation from its home bases. The RAF in the UK had the most up-to-date aircraft and the shortest lines of support. However when it came to other active areas like the Middle East, North Africa and the Far East, the RAF was at the end of its supply lines and spare parts were often in short supply. This resulted from a number of problems such as some part numbers failing to meet demand, UK RAF priorities, losses due to enemy action in transit and the prevailing operating conditions. In the early part of the War the RAF was forced to commit large numbers of aircraft to the desert campaigns without air intake filters. The sand is all pervading, not only from the Khamsins and Siroccos [**66**], but also from the miniature sandstorms blown up by propellers. No aero engine likes sand and the wear and tear was severe. In particular, crankshafts, cylinder liners and blade rod bearing tracks were major sufferers [**67, 68**].

It is much to the credit of the RAF engineer officers, aided by a few Rolls-Royce overhaul engineers, who utilised every available repair scheme and thought up some of their own, that they kept the repair lines going.

Having lapped steps out of worn crankshaft journals, they topped main bearing shells, fitted shims behind the bearings and then line reamed back to size. When lead plating came in they would also plate above drawing size, but one had to take care because if too thick the lead would squeeze out and cause trouble. When crankshaft grinding facilities were installed it was possible to re-nitride crankshafts. After nitriding, one must lap the loose white nitrides from the surface removing about .0015 in from the diameter. Attempts were made on production and repair to do this by grinding, but it caused grinding cracks in the radius of the pin or journal leading to crank failures in service.

All manner of processes including plating by chromium, nickel and copper were used to restore worn surfaces and fitting diameters. Chromium was popular because of its hardness but could not be used on stressed components, due to the loss of fatigue strength caused by hydrogen embrittlement, although with today's knowledge and processes it can be used more widely without danger.

The worst problem was cylinder wear, which occurred at the top of the liner on the thrust side at the changeover point of the top ring, and this created a serious shortage of liners. One had to grind liners oversize to eliminate the step to enable them to be used again, but no one would then countenance oversize pistons because of interchangeability problems. One therefore had to turn out engines with lives that would be shortened by oil consumption or ring gumming due to oversize liners. It was far better than wringing one's hands and, having regard to engine mortality rates for all reasons, it kept aircraft flying. The answer was hard chrome plating at the top of the liner and this was introduced on both new and repair engines. It was not without its difficulties. Chromium has a problem of wetability and it was not easy to get piston rings to bed properly, in spite of lapping cylinder liners. It was Sunbeam Talbot who, using a special lapping powder (Goldsworthy's 6X) and a sort of reciprocating spiral action lavatory brush, produced a satin finish which held oil. Somewhat refined it became the standard liner finish and with high Brinell liners (550 hardness) was the final cure.

Liner wear was at its worst in the UK on Merlin Xs in Whitley Vs assigned to Coastal Command, glider towing and training. Merlin X production had ceased, attrition rates were low, and in consequence aircraft were powered by second and third life engines, often with .010 in oversize liners. Coastal Command, using long range high boost/low revs cruise with 100 per cent glycol cooling, ran into a lot of ring gumming due to high piston temperatures and blow by. Finally it was agreed, for the Merlin X only, to fit a .010 in oversize piston which was a vast improvement, but with priority going to the operating squadrons.

The Whitley installation [70] had a quirk which was never understood. Some Merlins would have oil loss from the crankcase breather at high power which led to the introduction of the rocker cover breather system on later types. Oil loss was more common on engines with wide piston clearances but the Whitley heavily exaggerated any breather loss. With training units doing a lot of high power circuits and bumps ring gumming was not a problem, but breather loss was.

One particular station, No. 42 Operational Training Unit at Ashbourne, complained bitterly and, having checked on their engine hours, I concluded that until we could get engines with lower piston clearances, and this could not be for some time, replacement engines would not on average be much better. I went to the Station, saw the Chief Technical Officer and explained the situation, formal communications within the RAF not being that rapid on such matters. The training staff on the Station who were operational pilots on rest between tours were unused to the problem and did not like it. We went down to the Whitley training flight, met the flight commander and went to look at the aeroplanes. The breather loss was so severe that not only was oil dripping off the trailing edge of the wing but also from the tailplane. I checked the Form 700s and surprisingly oil consumptions overall were well within limits. After some discussion the flight commander agreed that I would fly with him on the worst aircraft and if I then thought the engines were OK he would accept my decision. So he flew me that afternoon on the two aircraft that no-one wanted to fly. It was no good just ground running the engines at take-off power because it was not until the aircraft had reached about 80 knots that the trouble started and just at the point of unstick there was a solid jet of black oil pouring from the breathers of both engines. This continued until after cleaning up the aircraft and throttling back into the climb, when the oil loss began to decrease and finally died away until there was just an oil haze from the outlets. We spent the whole afternoon doing circuits and bumps and in spite of having two very oily aeroplanes I passed them as being serviceable. He was a bit surprised because they did look most unpleasant, but we agreed that he would put them back into use and that I would recheck them after a further period of training flights. He also agreed that I would fly with every aircraft showing the problem and if I periodically checked them for deterioration he would accept the situation. This I did and we developed mutual confidence, thus managing our way out of the problem until higher standard engines came along. I have been into this story at some length because other Rolls-Royce personnel have done more difficult things with other squadrons. Such was the rapport between the Company and the RAF, which stemmed from the basic reliability of the engine and Hives' confidence gaining gestures which built up faith in the engines throughout the services.

The perspective
In August 1945 the years of military endeavour and power development on the Merlin suddenly stopped, but had the War not ended, more horsepower and more altitude performance would have been available.

A three speed supercharger drive interchangeable with the existing mechanism had been fully tested and there were schemes to improve further the air entry into the supercharger.

The milestones of the Merlin are summarised in the charts following the appendices but some additional facts are of interest. During the War years the Merlin powered more than 50,000 single engined fighters, covering every operational fighter role. It was the only British engine to be used by the Americans in an American combat aircraft. Although fully cleared, the 2,200 hp RM17SM did not enter service but post War the 130 series powered the de Havilland Hornet, a long range twin-engined single-seat fighter which served with the RAF at home and overseas [71]. It was the RAF's fastest piston engined fighter with a maximum speed of 472 mph. A development of the Lancaster, the Lincoln, just failed to see War service but it became the mainstay of Bomber Command post War and continued in service until 1955, from 1951 being gradually replaced by the Avon powered Canberra and later the 'V' bombers. Although early aircraft were fitted with two stage Merlin 85s (a Merlin 66 equivalent), squadron aircraft used the Packard built 68As.

The Merlin 140 for the Short Sturgeon [72] embodied a number of departures from past military practice. Most obviously it had a contra-rotating reduction gear but the general engine design followed the new civil Merlin 620 series, first used by Trans Canada Airlines. Mechanically it was similar to the 100 series, having end feed lubrication and single point SU injection but the cylinder blocks embodied the detailed refinements aimed at longer lives in civil operation. Externally it had what was loosely known as an 'all white finish', again in line with civil practice. This meant that all aluminium castings had a scratch brushed and emery dressed finish devoid of paint or enamel, while pipework was in stainless steel. All external studs, bolts, nuts and washers were cadmium plated to match. Technically this meant reducing all the torque loading figures on external fixings, because the self lubricating properties of cadmium plate transmitted a higher tensile load to the bolt or stud. A welcome feature was an auxiliary gearbox in the aircraft thus freeing the engine from the various aircraft accessories.

Comparisons tend to be invidious but of the other allied engines of the War period, the Pratt and Whitney R 2800 showed a high degree of versatility in operational types and over 105,000 were built. In its later forms it gave 2,300 hp but being 70 per cent bigger than the Merlin its specific power was a lot less and it lacked the absolute altitude power of the Merlin even when turbo-supercharged. Of the British engines 105,000 Bristol Hercules were built taking into account post War and licensee manufacture. Because it always lacked altitude performance its potential was limited and a two stage super-charged version never came on production. It was at its excellent best when employed in tactical and anti-shipping roles in the various marks of Beaufighter.

Students of technically advanced engines often use the Napier Sabre as a basis for assessing the Merlin, taking, as a yardstick, the very high test bed powers demonstrated around the end of the War. Operationally it was used solely in the Hawker Typhoon and Tempest, essentially low altitude aircraft, and gave the RAF its initial ability to catch the Fw190 at low level. Both types performed outstanding service in the period following the invasion of France in tactical roles. Total wartime production of aircraft consisted of 3,330 Typhoons plus 800 Tempest V. Post War there was a run of 140 Tempest VIs. Total engines, including spares, amounted to between 3 and 4 months average wartime Merlin output. Its high revving 24 cylinder construction endowed it with high specific powers at low altitude. However, using the criteria of actual powers employed in the squadrons during the war period, there is no firm evidence that any Sabre flew at higher power per litre or cubic inch than the Merlin 66. This engine, of which some 8,000 were produced for Spitfires (including the 266 Packard equivalent), gave 1,745 hp at 3,000 rpm, +18 lb boost in MS gear on 100 octane fuel from 1943 onwards and 2,050 hp at 3,000 rpm, +25 lb boost on 150 grade fuel from early in 1944.

In early squadron service, the Sabre proved unreliable and led to a difficult period of operations. It also had the habit of being difficult to start, particularly during the winter. Air Marshal Sir Dennis Crowley-Milling is a very experienced Fighter Pilot, who flew with Douglas Bader's 242 Hurricane Squadron in the Battle of Britain and later flew Spitfires on cross-Channel operations. When the Typhoon came into use he formed and commanded one of the first squadrons. I have been able to discuss this experience with him and he confirms that although the Typhoon was fast at low level it lacked altitude performance and there were too many forced landings due to engine problems. This led him to visit Napier to express his disquiet with the situation, which in his view arose from the engine still requiring a lot of development. Pilots with Merlin backgrounds treated the Sabre with caution. However a great deal of effort was made by Napier and post War when he commanded a wing of Tempest VIs in the Middle East, which used the Sabre V engine, reliability was much improved. I am indebted to Sir Dennis for his authoritative comments.

The big Bristol Centaurus saw War service only in the Vickers Warwick, the Tempest II being in squadron service post War.

The question is often asked as to how the Merlin compared with enemy frontline equipment. A book could be written on this subject but the following brief comparisons can be made.

The Battle of Britain has been well documented in 'The Narrow Margin'*. Although the Hurricane did more of the fighting, the Spitfire was the faster aeroplane and at around 20,000 ft it had the performance edge on the Me109. When

---

* Derek Wood & Derek Dempster published by Arrow Books 1969 and now out of print.

the enemy abandoned the tactic of escorted bomber formations and resorted to high flying fighter bombers it was evident that at around 30,000 ft the Me109 was slightly quicker and climbed faster than the Spitfire. Graphs would indicate that the Daimler Benz DB601 engine had marginally more combat power than the Merlin III at altitude. In 1941 the Spitfire V was equal with the 109F in terms of speed and climb.

At the end of 1941 the enemy produced a considerable again with the Fw190 powered by the BMW801. This aircraft could outrun and outclimb the Spitfire V. The engine was giving 1,450 hp at around 16,000 ft, an advantage of some 250 hp over the Merlin 45/46 in the Spitfire V at this height.

By mid 1942 the Merlin 61 in the Spitfire IX was giving 1,300 hp at 25,000 ft, putting the Spitfire on top at this altitude. However, in the 15/20,000 ft band the Merlin was running throttled and did not have a clear advantage. In 1943 Lovesey introduced the Merlin 66, which had somewhat lower gear ratios in the supercharger but a bigger first stage impeller, giving more than 1,600 hp at over 16,000 ft, and it is accepted that the Spitfire IX with the Merlin 66 was outstanding at these altitudes. Equally, on 150 grade fuel with over 2,000 hp available, it made the Spitfire IX a superb lower level fighter. The Merlin 61 was superseded by the Merlin 70, which had the 66 blower with 61 gear ratios, giving a marked increase in the high altitude performance. It will therefore be seen that the variously rated two stage Merlins provided the RAF with 'horses for courses' to meet the various altitude cases.

Power development on the DB600 series engines followed the route of increasing rpm with longer valve timings rather than major increases in boost pressure. Based on Experimental Department reports it is clear that, including the DB605A, this range of engines could not match the two stage Merlins in terms of maximum power or altitude performance, in spite of being some 25 per cent larger in cubic capacity.

The BMW801 was a very advanced powerplant when it came into service. The 14 cylinder, two row, 42 litre, aircooled radial was 55 per cent bigger than the Merlin in capacity and was unique in having geared fan cooling and close cowling. Experimental Department reports suggest that an uprating was being introduced, using more boost and rpm, which would make it about equal to the Merlin 66 but with a more rapid power decay at high altitude. It must also be borne in mind that the Fw190 had an all-up weight about 1,500 lb greater than the Spitfire IX which affected the power to weight ratio.

The enemy also had power boosting systems and although nitrous oxide is often talked of as a medium, water methanol injection was generally used. Either would give a considerable power increase for a period but entailed the weight and complication of an extra system. Certainly the BMW801 had the reputation of being brittle if operational limitations were exceeded and there were restrictions on the use of water methanol. The Daimler Benz engines had hydraulically driven superchargers, which allowed the speed of the blower to be varied, so that at lower altitudes the intake to the supercharger was not throttled. In practice the drive tended to sludge, reducing supercharger performance.

Later in the War 190s were seen with Daimler Benz and Junkers Jumo powerplants. Although advanced versions of these engines were under development with two-stage two-speed superchargers, they do not appear to have reached squadron service. It seems therefore that the engines used were the same as those fitted to Me109s and Ju88s.

Although what has been said is somewhat generalised it will be seen that Rolls-Royce dealt with the challenge and showed great flexibility in getting more powerful engines into service. Significantly power developments were achieved by exploiting the boost potential allowed by improved fuels. The philosophy behind this was that it eliminated extra systems and enabled maximum power to be used as long as one had petrol. The only exception was the small number of Mosquito night fighters fitted with nitrous oxide injection to their single stage Merlins for a specific purpose. These aircraft were superseded by the Mk30 with two stage high altitude engines.

In summary therefore, apart from the high altitude case in the Battle of Britain and a period when the Fw190 first came into service, Rolls-Royce were always able to provide the power from the Merlin to complement improved Spitfires and maintain a highly effective position. This also applied to the Merlin Mustang. The Mosquito made impressive gains in performance with more powerful Merlins and it was still the pre-eminent twin at the end of the War. This does not take into account the Merlin 113/114 high altitude versions then entering service in fighters.

Rolls-Royce also did not neglect the two stage Griffon and in combat the Spitfire XIV was a formidable aeroplane with over 1,800 hp available at 21,000 ft. It had the advantage of the Rotol five bladed propeller, which was very efficient at height and these features gave the aircraft a maximum speed of 448 mph at 26,000 ft and an excellent altitude performance. The first kill by the Allied Forces of an Me262 jet fighter was claimed by a Spitfire XIV of 401 Squadron.

However the gas turbine, whose engineering teams have changed the face of aviation, rapidly took over. In the military field it has brought massive increases in aircraft performance and offensive capability to air force commanders in ways not possible with the piston engine. In civil flying faraway places are within the reach of inexpensive package tours, but if one has the money New York is within 3 hours of London flying in luxury at 1,400 mph at an altitude of 60,000 ft. The gas turbine has provided much greater reliability than the piston engine with much longer overhaul lives and the 'on condition' philosophy.

The inspiration behind the entire Merlin programme following the death of Sir Henry Royce was *Hs*, later Lord Hives. He wrought its success with his team of often turbulent barons and an army of workers. Most importantly he had the inestimable contribution of the Ford Motor Company in England, the Packard Motor Company in Detroit and a host of suppliers, subcontractors and repairers.

Some names have been mentioned in the text but Arthur Rubbra will always be associated with the design of the engine and its variants. Cyril Lovesey, the doyen of development engineers, did the almost impossible in bringing together so many conflicting demands and turning them into a highly effective range of engines.

Many more who contributed are also no longer with us and I hope that the diminishing band of survivors will not take it amiss if I draw on just two names from that honourable company, Sir Stanley Hooker and Geoff Wilde, for their work on supercharger development, which contributed so greatly to the engine.

In 1587 Sir Francis Drake, in a despatch to Sir Francis Walsingham, wrote 'There must be a beginning of any great matter, but the continuing unto the end until it be thoroughly finished yields the true glory'. It is, I think, a fitting comment on Lord Hives.

Appendix I

The Packard Merlin

It is recognised that apart from the occasional reference this booklet has concerned itself with British built Merlins. This is because my responsibilities concentrated on these types, Packard engines being handled separately by Glasgow. While there was good liaison on major issues the day to day problems were handled directly with Packard and I did not feel that I could write with authority on this subject.

However, as there is considerable interest in the Packard product the following comments may be helpful. Packard engines for the RAF consisted of engines for Lancasters, Mosquitos and Spitfires. Early engines were Merlin 28s, rather similar to the Merlin XX but with a two piece block designed in America. The Merlin 38s were equivalent to Merlin 22s and used the Rolls-Royce design of two piece cylinder block, as did later engines. The 224 was equivalent to the 24. All these engines were for use in Lancasters and it is interesting that 617 Squadron was using 224 powered aircraft on the Dams raid. The 225 was similar to the 25 and fitted in the Mosquito. The Merlin 266 was similar to Merlin 66 and was installed in the Spitfire XVI. Packard engines for the USAAF took the nomenclature V.1650 with slash numbers to denote mark number. They were visually identified by a propeller shaft with SAE standard splines. Mustangs for the RAF were fitted with V.1650/3 or V.1650/7, two stage engines with 63 and 66 ratings. Post War RAF Lincolns were fitted with 68A engines, which again were similar to the 66.

Technically the major difference between Rolls-Royce and Packard Merlins was the supercharger drive, the latter using epicyclic gearing instead of the Farman drive. Naturally, American magnetos and Bendix carburettors were used. Some 100 series equivalents were built at the end of the War with the Simmonds fuel control units and these were installed in later Mustangs.

As one would expect, Packard built engines to very high standards of quality. Technical problems were not dissimilar from those experienced on British engines and when comparing like with like modification standards there was nothing to choose between engine sources.

At Squadron level there were times when there were fortuitous variations in reliability either way but when dealing with large numbers of engines at Group or Command level there was good consistency in results between British and Packard engines. The 60,000 engines produced by Packard for the RAF and USAAF were of inestimable value.

Supplement to Appendix I

In Appendix I it has been stated that the Lancaster IIIs of 617 Squadron were equipped with Merlin 224s (Packard built Merlin 24s). This was not the case, the Squadron being equipped with Merlin 28s (Packard build Merlin 22s but with their own type of two-piece block).

The single piece block engines (Merlins IIs, IIIs and XXs) were rated at 12 lb boost and following the introduction of the two-piece block (on 22s, 23s, 28s and 38s), the boost pressures were increased to 14 lb/sq in in MS gear and 16 lb/sq in FS gear. Further increases in boost pressure to 18 lb/sq in followed the introduction of further modifications notably the blended radius connecting rod (Mod 587) and the double girder pistons (Mod 742) in the Merlin 24s, 224s, 25s, 26s and 27s.

The ratings (with cut-out pulled) of the Merlin 28s were:

Sea level MS gear, 14 lb/sq in boost, 3,000 rpm, 1,420 hp
           FS gear, 16 lb/sq in boost, 3,000 rpm, 1,350 hp

FT height MS gear, 14 lb/sq in boost, 3,000 rpm, 1,480 hp, 5,500 ft
           FS gear, 16 lb/sq in boost, 3,000 rpm, 1,460 hp, 10,500 ft

Appendix II

Terminology

It has been suggested that as this booklet was written in the argot of its time some explanation of terms like 'mod' and mark number would help.

These notes are not exhaustive but are sufficient unto the day.

When a new type of engine comes onto production the collection of drawings defining it and enabling it to be made are covered by a DIS (Drawing Introductory Sheet). Broadly at the point of release to production the DIS is sealed, meaning that it can no longer be changed without a formal procedure.

This procedure is known as a modification (mod), removing obsolete parts from the DIS and adding new ones. The modification is given a number and the engine log book will contain not only the DIS number, but all modifications embodied, so that the user knows the precise standard of each engine.

Important modifications may need to be embodied either in the field or at repair, and each modification is categorised so that its priority for embodiment is understood and acted on accordingly.

An engine mark number defines to the user the engine rating, special installation features (eg electric or cartridge starting, provision of cabin blower drive, hand of rotation etc). It may also just define a special mod standard (eg the first Merlins for transport aircraft were Merlin 24s and when fitted with mods to improve engine life became T24). Thus engines of several mark numbers can have the same rating.

There are also experimental nomenclature numbers. These were used by the Ministry of Aircraft Production (MAP) to define experimental types and in particular the power rating and Merlins were categorised, as an example, RM10SM, 'R' standing for Rolls-Royce, 'M' for Merlin, 10 would be the number. S and M showed that it had a two speed supercharger, 'S' being full or high speed and 'M' moderate or low speed. A single speed rating would just have the appropriate letter.

These numbers were used because some experimental projects did not come to production when the engine would be given a mark number. This is why the RM17SM is referred to in this way. Although fully type tested, it was dropped because the War ended and there was no longer a need for it.

This nomenclature was often used by Rolls-Royce engineers because it encapsulated for them an engine rating, with all the features to give that performance.

Appendix III

Other Merlin applications

In concentrating on the main stream use of the Merlin some aspects were omitted to prevent the story being obscured by too much detail. With a second edition it seems worthwhile to fill in some omissions.

The Seafire, a Naval version of the Spitfire, is the most important. The Fleet Air Arm did not have an effective British fighter in the early days of the war and the Seafire was a welcome addition [87]. In Merlin form it did not progress beyond the Merlin 45/55 family but later production used the 55M with a two piece block and cropped supercharger rotor. Rated at 18 lb at low level it gave good performance for Naval operations. The Seafire performed better than the Sabre or Centaurus Fire brand, which was dropped from the fighter role on this account. Later developments of the Seafire were Griffon powered, but some Merlin Seafires were fitted with 4-bladed propellers and stub exhausts, making them look like the Spitfire IX. The Fleet Air Arm used the Fairey Barracuda as a torpedo carrier or dive bomber [**58**]. It was a large aeroplane that made its Merlin 32 work hard for its living. One problem was over-revving in the dive when, on occasion, the propeller system could not control the rpm. This could lead to big end failures or a propeller blade pulling out of the hub, when the out of balance forces would rip the top half of the reduction gear from the engine.

There was argument about these failures, but the Merlin always showed when it had been over-revved. Exhaust valve bounce would cause the top valve spring washer to hammer the exhaust valve guide, causing heavy burrs. Because other makes of engines could lose reduction gears as a primary failure there was a tendency to think that the Merlin did the same thing, but this was not the case. Post war there was one accident to a Hornet, a complete gear breaking away from the engine with the propeller intact. On examination all the casing fractures were found to be of a sudden overload nature. The Accidents Investigation Branch, with whom we were working, were able to show that the cause was a cowling panel on the powerplant coming adrift. It was sucked into the low pressure area at the propeller blade root and fouled a propeller blade, the unbalance tearing away the reduction gear. This was the only case where a gear had come adrift without a propeller blade pulling out first.

The losses of Fairey Battles in 1940 made some members of the RAF look with regret at the Hawker Henley [88]. This two-seat bomber based on Hurricane technology would have been a far more useful aircraft with which to combat the

German advance into France, but it was relegated to target towing at Air Gunnery Schools. The Hawker Hotspur [89] and Boulton Paul Defiant [90] were single Merlin two-seat fighters, the armament being a 4-gun turret behind the pilot. The Hotspur was a one-off but the Defiant reached squadron service. After initial success against bombers it suffered badly in fighter to fighter combat because it lacked performance and had a restricted field of fire. The type had to be withdrawn from daylight operations, but in the night fighter role it was credited with the highest number of kills per interception of any night fighter type in the Winter of 1940/41.

The Sea Hurricane was an adaptation for catapult launch from merchant ships for convoy defence. The engines were Merlin IIIs, running at full throttle for maximum sea level power. Having regard to the hazards of sea water corrosion with the limited inhibition possible, the engines worked well. It was a tough, dangerous operation for the pilots, who generally had to bale out at the end of the sortie and depend upon being picked up by a ship.

Reference has been made to the expertise of the RAF in repairing engines suffering wear and tear from desert operations. This work was just one initiative in the technical field, but under the pressure of war more adventurous tasks were undertaken. In 1942 in the Middle East the Germans were making high altitude reconnaissance flights which were not being intercepted. In the absence of Merlins with two-stage superchargers a small number of Merlin 46s were locally up-rated. This was done by raising the compression and providing ignition timing controlled from the cockpit. The change to compression ratio required a great deal of work, reducing cylinder block heights, modifying combustion chambers to provide piston clearance and re-matching induction pipes and inclined drive shafts. These were installed in Spitfires which had been cleaned up and lightened. The result was that successful interceptions were made at heights of well over 40,000 ft. If my memory serves me correctly, Wg/Cdr Stainforth was one of the pilots.

There were various aircraft which did not reach squadron service. The Vickers Windsor was a heavy bomber, fitted with 4 Merlin 85s, in Vickers designed power plants [91]. The Westland Welkin was a single-seat high altitude fighter, powered by Merlin 70 series and not unlike the Whirlwind [92]. Over 60 were built, including one two-seat night fighter. It was probably a casualty of the successful Mosquito, which covered so many operational roles, something that other manufacturers also felt. Early in the war Miles Aircraft, who built the Master trainer with the Kestrel XXX, produced a prototype fighter, the M20 fitted with a single-stage Merlin [93]. It was largely of wood construction and was stated to be very light, carrying 50 per cent more fuel than a Hurricane. However, as its performance fell below that of the contemporary Spitfire, it did not meet the needs of Fighter Command.

North American Aviation produced a scaled down version of their outstanding Merlin Mustang, which was brought to England and flown at Boscombe Down. Known as the Margie Hart it was probably the fastest single engined aircraft of its day, but was again a one-off. Before the war, Rolls-Royce were collaborating with French manufacturers and two prototypes were flying before June 1940. These were the Amiot 356 a twin-engined bomber [**94**], and the Dewoitine 520, a single-engined single-seat fighter. Both were powered by two-speed supercharged Merlin Xs.

During the War the Merlin was used in various non-aviation forms and the best known is the Meteor tank engine [**95**]. When it was seen how underpowered were British tanks, with 320 hp Liberty engines, Hives promoted an un-supercharged Merlin in this application. It offered many advantages. Its technology was well understood and at 500 hp gave the power the tanks needed, with a good power to weight ratio, but at modest engine loadings. It could therefore use parts unsuitable for aero work and also serviceable components taken from crash damaged aero engines. The task of developing and producing the Meteor as it was called, was given to *Rm* and his team at Clan Foundry in Belper, but assembly was undertaken by Henry Meadows. Development progress was rapid, but Clan engineers found that they were impeded by the general unreliability of tanks. In typical Rolls-Royce fashion they took on tank development so that testing could be carried out in the vehicle without hold-ups. When the Meteor-powered Cromwell went ahead it was built by the Birmingham Carriage and Wagon Company with Clan looking after the dynamics of the vehicle and the result was a very successful tank. It is not altogether surprising that the engine was treated with apathy by some sections of MOS and in 1941 *Hs* was compelled to write to Lord Beaverbrook, who was Minister of Aircraft Production, and had encouraged the project complaining of lack of progress and asking for his help.

In 1943 Hives exchanged the Meteor for Rover's Gas Turbine interests. Rover continued to develop the engine for a number of years. Post-War, among other changes, fuel injection was introduced in place of Zenith carburettors, the power going up to over 800 hp. The Meteor engines are still in service in various parts of the world, including the Middle East.

A marine version of the Merlin was built for high speed craft for the Coastal Forces of the Royal Navy and about 70 were delivered before the project was abandoned to give priority to aero engines at an early stage in the War [**96**]. The engine was a Merlin III with direct drive and a U shaped air intake to connect with the installation in the ship and finished in cream enamel. My contact with the engine was to run a course at the Aero Instruction School annexe at Nightingale Road for Polish Naval personnel (the crew of the submarine Orzel), my qualification being that I had a working knowledge of technical French. None of the party spoke English but the Lieutenant in Command had a little French and this was our tenuous link. Somehow we finished the course and stayed friends in spite of the difficulties. It was a fair example of wartime improvisation.

To this day heavily boosted Packard Merlins are the choice of many of the top speedboat racers [97] in such events as the Gold Cup, and like their pylon racing counterparts in Mustangs still have a considerable future.

Finally, Mike Evans has reminded me of a very little known installation. Air Commodore Helmore, known for his inventiveness in such things as the Helmore Havoc, conceived the idea of a Meteor-powered torpedo to destroy enemy capital ships. One was built at Hucknall and certainly in-water tests were carried out. The idea was that the torpedo was dropped from a heavy bomber like a Lincoln and under radio command from the aircraft proceeded just below the surface, the engine breathing through a schnorkel mast. At an appropriate range from the enemy the command aircraft could submerge the torpedo to its operating depth, the engine breathing from compressed air cylinders for the attack. It was apparently taken very seriously and was stopped only by the end of hostilities, its objective being the major units of the Japanese Fleet.

Appendix IV

The Merlin and 100 Octane Fuel

Questions have been asked on the early user of 100 octane fuel and in particular on its influence during the Battle of Britain. Until 1937 the Merlin had been confined to 87 octane fuel to DTD230, because it was felt that in the event of war 100 octane, which was being developed by the Americans, might not be available to the British. This anxiety arose from the American Neutrality Act, which could prevent supplies being shipped to this country. Probably as the result of a paper by Rod Banks in January 1937, the Air Ministry agreed to proceed with engine development to take advantage of high octane fuel.

At that time the American 100 octane did not suit the Merlin because it lacked a good 'rich mixture response'. Esso undertook the development of a suitable fuel, using 10% aromatics, and the driving force behind this was Dr Bill Sweeney whose fuel mix became known as Sweeney's Blend. Three months before the start of the war an Esso tanker *Beaconhill* delivered a full cargo of the special 100 octane fuel to Britain and by March 1940 the decision had been taken to switch Fighter Command to this type. Bomber Command changed over early in 1941.

The effect of 100 octane was to allow the Merlin to run at 12 lb boost, putting up the power of the Merlin III from just over 1,000 hp to 1,300 hp. However, this high power was obtained at between 8,000 and 9,000 ft and above this altitude at a max combat power rpm of 3,000 the boost and, therefore, power advantage was progressively declining. On 87 octane fuel and 6 lb boost, using 3,000 rpm, the maximum power was 1,030 hp at 16,000 ft. At this point on either fuel the engine was giving the same power, so above this height 100 octane fuel offered no advantage. The majority of the air fighting in the Battle of Britain was at 18,000 ft and above and the engine in most common use was the Merlin III. The gain in performance from 100 octane was entirely at lower altitudes. Before the end of the Battle Spitfire IIs with Merlin XIIs were in service, with the supercharger gear ratio increased from 8.58 to 9.09:1 giving a better full throttle height at 12 lb boost and a small number of Hurricane IIs fitted with two-speed Merlin IIs, with ratios of 8.15 and 9.49:1 for MS and FS gear, these engines could take much greater advantage of 100 octane fuel and in the case of the Merlin XX were capable of maintaining 12 lb boost to over 20,000 ft at 3,000 rpm, thanks to the new central entry supercharger.

This set the pattern and without 100 octane fuel the further power development of the Merlin would not have been possible. As an example, the two stage blown Merlin 66 was capable of over 1,600 hp at 16,000 ft using 3,000 rpm and 18 lb boost. The pioneering work of Esso to produce a suitable 100 octane fuel was the key to the high power Merlins in all spheres of operation and it was not until 1944 when 150 grade fuel became available that further advances to boost pressure to 25 lb were made, allowing over 2,000 hp to be used in squadron service.

The opening paragraphs of this appendix are the result of information supplied to Michael Evans, Chairman of the Rolls-Royce Heritage Trust, by Alexander Ogston, Historian of the Wings Club in New York, who has had a lifetime in fuel technology, and a conversation which I had with Rod Banks shortly before his death.

The military
Merlin family

Merlin I

single stage
single speed
supercharger;
ramp head

Battle

Single stage, single speed

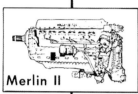

Merlin II

Spitfire I
Hurricane
Battle

Merlin XII/30

Spitfire—II
Barracuda

Merlin 45/46

Spitfire V

Single stage, 2 speed

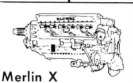

Merlin X

Whitley
Wellington
Halifax

Merlin XX series

Hurricane
Lancaster
Beaufighter
Mosquito
Halifax
Lancastrian
Defiant

2 stage, 2 speed, intercooled

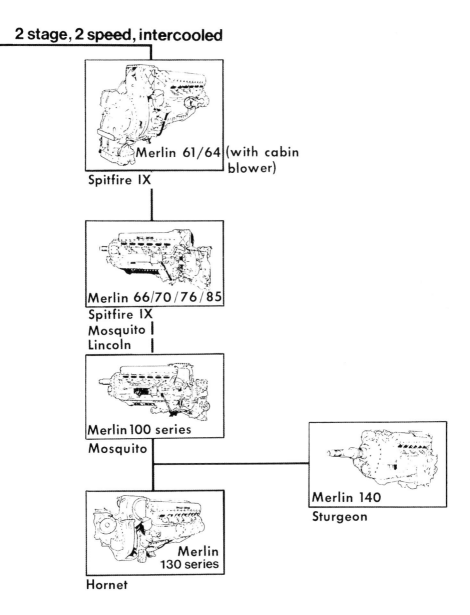

Merlin 61/64 (with cabin blower)

Spitfire IX

Merlin 66/70/76/85

Spitfire IX
Mosquito
Lincoln

Merlin 100 series

Mosquito

Merlin 140

Sturgeon

Merlin 130 series

Hornet

MERLIN SUMMARY
PERFORMANCE DEVELOPMENT

DURING THE PERIOD UNDER REVIEW THE FOLLOWING PARTICULARS REMAIN UNCHANGED:

CUBIC CAPACITY   27 LITRES (1 650 CUBIC INCH)
COMPRESSION RATIO   6:1
COMBAT RPM   3,000

	1939 MERLIN III	1944 MERLIN 66
COMBAT POWER	1,030 HP	2,050 HP
	3,000 RPM	3,000 RPM
	+6 1/4 lb BOOST	+25lb BOOST
ALTITUDE AT WHICH ENGINE WOULD GIVE 1 000 HP AT FULL THROTTLE AND 3 000 RPM.	16,000 ft	30,000 ft (MERLIN 61 IN SERVICE JUNE 1942) 36,000 ft (MERLIN 113/114)
HP PER CUBIC INCH	0.6	1.24
POUNDS (NET DRY) PER HP	1.4	0.8
OPERATING ALTITUDES	SEA LEVEL TO 32,000 ft	SEA LEVEL TO 47,000 ft (SPECIAL SPITFIRE MK VII, SAMPLE PRODUCTION SPITFIRE IXs FLOWN TO 46,000 ft BY ALEX HENSHAW)

MAXIMUM TYPE TESTED HP (RM17SM, 3,000 RPM + 30lb BOOST) - 2,200 HP
MAXIMUM FLIGHT CLEARANCE TESTED POWER (RM17SM) - 2,340 HP
MAXIMUM ENDURANCE TEST POWER (3,000 RPM + 36lb BOOST, WATER INJECTION) - 2,640 HP
LONGEST HIGH POWER DEVELOPMENT TEST, 100 HOURS AT 3,000 RPM + 18lb BOOST, TWO SUCCESSFUL TESTS

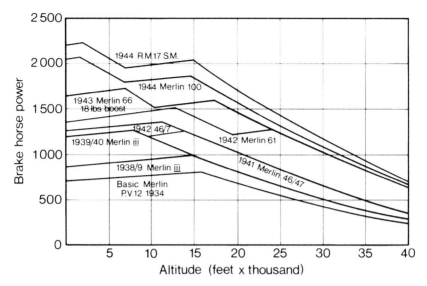

33 Performance comparison

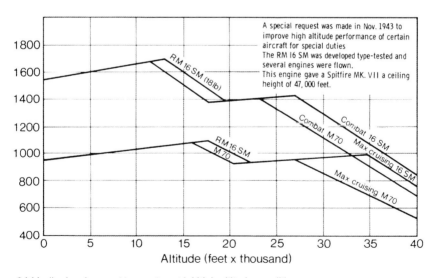

34 Merlin development to meet special high altitude conditions

SUMMARY OF LOGISTICS AND ENGINE LIVES

TOTAL PRODUCTION (4 UK AND 1 US SOURCE)	160,000 (100,000 PLUS IN UK)
MARKS OF ENGINE	52
OPERATIONAL AIRCRAFT TYPES	19
REPAIR ENGINE OUTPUT 6 UK SOURCES & RAF OVERSEAS BASES	50,000 RAF OVERSEAS OUTPUT NOT INCLUDED

ENGINE LIVES

	1939	1944/45
FIGHTERS	240 HOURS	300/360 HOURS
BOMBERS	300 HOURS	360/420 HOURS
TRANSPORT		480/500 HOURS
PERCENTAGE OF TOTAL ENGINES TO REACH TIME EXPIRY PASSING THROUGH REPAIR ORGANISATION FROM 1942 ONWARDS		AVERAGE 35%
AVERAGE LIFE OF ENGINE PASSING THROUGH REPAIR ORGANISATION FROM 1942 ONWARDS		APPROXIMATELY 60% OF NOMINAL LIFE FOR TYPE

35 Hawker Horsley flying testbed at Hucknall. Ray Dorey is fifth from right

36 Toura Caves near Cairo

37 Back streets of Cairo

38 Avro York

39 Avro Lancastrian

40 Avro Tudor

41 Canadair DC4M

42 Avro Lincoln

43 Fairey Battle

44 Merlin Whitley V

45 Merlin Wellington

46 Merlin Halifax

47 Avro Lancaster

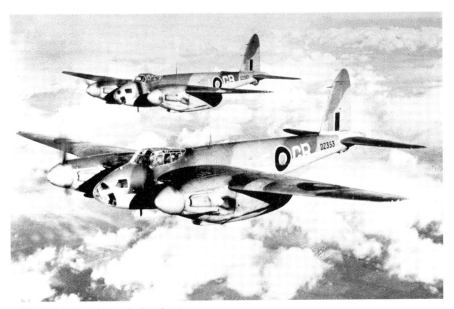

48 de Havilland Mosquito bombers

49 Mosquito night fighter

50 Spitfire VB

51 Early Spitfire IX – Merlin 61

52 Spitfire IX with Merlin 61

53 Hurricane at Brooklands

54 Hurricane II fighter bomber

55 Curtiss P40 – Packard Merlin

56 One of the first Merlin conversions – North American Mustang

57 Prototype Merlin Mustang installation

58 Barracuda

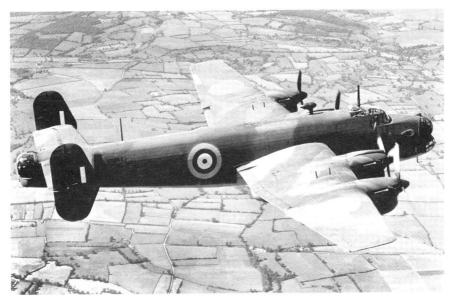

59 Merlin Halifax engine installations

60 Hucknall converted Mosquito with Lancaster powerplants

103

61 Griffon Spitfire

62 Mosquito Mk30 night fighter powered by two stage Merlin

63 Merlin Beaufighter

64 Clipped wing Spitfire V

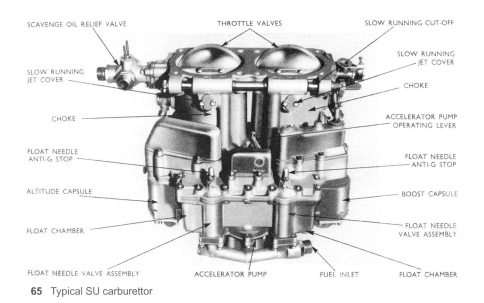

SCAVENGE OIL RELIEF VALVE   THROTTLE VALVES   SLOW RUNNING CUT-OFF

SLOW RUNNING
JET COVER

SLOW RUNNING
JET COVER

CHOKE

CHOKE

ACCELERATOR PUMP
OPERATING LEVER

FLOAT NEEDLE
ANTI-G STOP

FLOAT NEEDLE
ANTI-G STOP

ALTITUDE CAPSULE

BOOST CAPSULE

FLOAT CHAMBER

FLOAT NEEDLE
VALVE ASSEMBLY

FLOAT NEEDLE VALVE ASSEMBLY   ACCELERATOR PUMP   FUEL INLET   FLOAT CHAMBER

65 Typical SU carburettor

66 Desert sandstorm

106

67 Desert operations

68 Nose of Hurricane II showing air filter intake, oil and grime

107

69 Halifax in the Middle East

70 Whitley V

71 de Havilland Hornet

72 Short Sturgeon

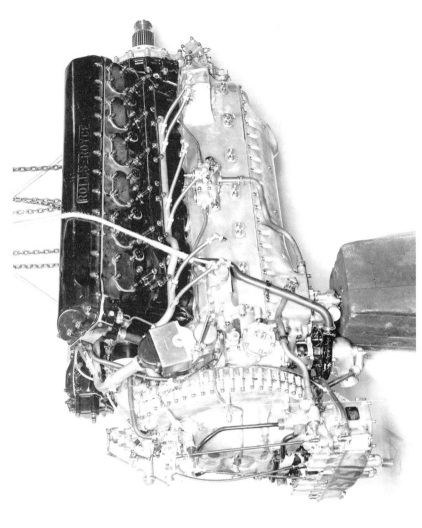

73 Merlin III. Typical early Merlin which powered Hurricane, Spitfire and Defiant in Battle of Britain and aircraft like Fairey Battle and Hawker Henley

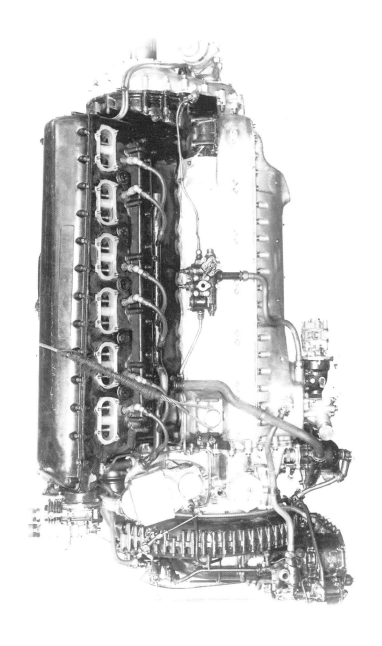

74 Merlin III complete with aircraft accessories including compressors, undercarriage pump and constant speed unit

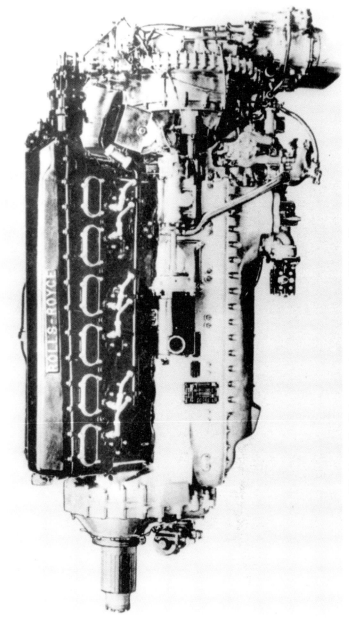

75 Merlin X with two speed supercharger for Whitley V and Wellington II

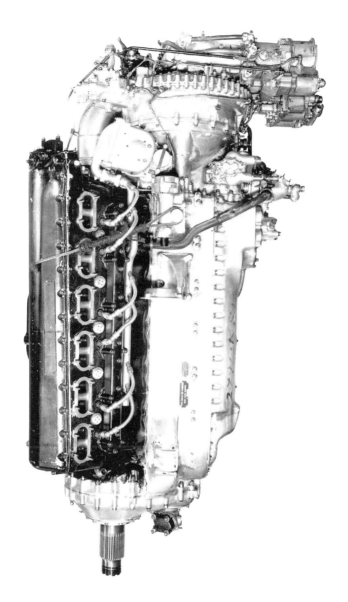

76 Merlin XX which powered Hurricane II, Beaufighter II, early Halifaxes and early Lancasters

77 Merlin 32 for Barracuda showing Coffman starter

78 Merlin 45/46 with central entry supercharger for Spitfire V

79 Two stage Merlin 60 series with cabin blower drive for Spitfire VII

80 Merlin 61 for Spitfire IX

81 Two stage Merlin 66 with Bendix injection carburettor

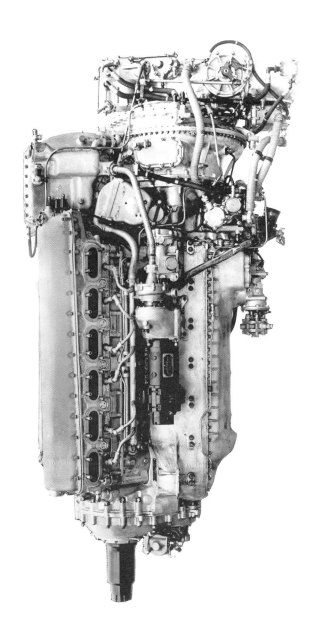

83 Merlin 130-133

120

84 Merlin 140 with contra-rotation reduction gear, unusually finished in black

85 Post War Merlin 620 series for Canadiar DC4M

86 Packard V1650-7 for Mustang

87 Supermarine Seafire with Merlin power, showing hook extended

88 Hawker Henley, unhappily used for target towing only

89 Hawker Hotspur two-seat fighter prototype

90 Boulton Paul Defiant, which proved more successful as a night fighter than in daylight operations

91 Vickers Armstrong Windsor bomber, four Merlin 85s in Vickers powerplants

92 Westland Welkin high altitude fighter

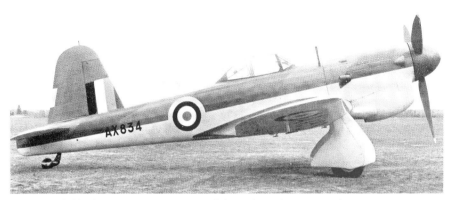

93 Miles M20 a Merlin powered prototype fighter of wooden construction

94 The French Amiot 356 bomber – two Merlin Xs. The Vichy Government used this aircraft for a number of flights between Vichy and Djibouti, following which it disappeared

95 Meteor tank engine showing its close resemblance to the Merlin. This example has two-piece cylinder blocks

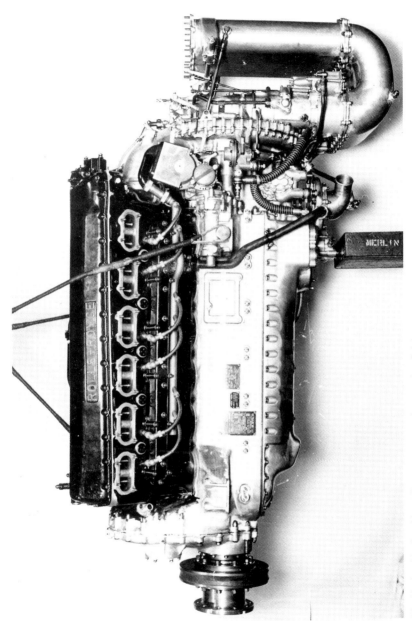

96 Marine Merlin without its cream enamel sea-going finish

129

97 Merlin-powered hydroplane, Slo-mo-shun V, at speed

98 About the same time as Merlin Xs were fitted to the Amiot 356 (see page 129) a version of the Dewotine 520D was also flying with a Merlin X. It is of interest that in 1940 prior to the German advance through Western Europe that Hives (*Hs*) reported in an internal memo that agreement had been reached with the French Government for the manufacture of the Merlin in France.

99 The Argentine Nancu fighter powered by Merlin 134-5 and 135-5 engines.

100 De Havilland Mosquito PR34 and Hornet – the two principal installations of the Merlin 100 series engines.

Courtesy of D Cox

Appendix V

The section headed 'The Perspective' discusses on page 71 performance comparisons between the Messerschmitt Bf109E and the Spitfire I during the Battle of Britain. Opinions formed during the Battle concluded that the Spitfire was the faster aeroplane at around 20,000 feet, but at higher altitudes the Bf109E was superior. Jeffrey Quill, who flew operationally in the Battle of Britain, takes the view that while the enemy had a slight edge on the Spitfire in rate of climb at low altitudes, above 20,000 feet the advantage lay with the Spitfire. He makes the point that the Bf109E achieved its best rate of climb at a lower forward airspeed than the Spitfire which meant that it would be climbing at a steeper angle than the Spitfire, although the Spitfire would be gaining height more quickly. In his book '*Birth of a Legend – the Spitfire*' he publishes official German figures which confirm his combat experience.

Air Commodore Alan Deere DSO, CBE, DFC and Bar, who fought in the operations over Dunkirk and throughout the Battle of Britain, finishing the war with 22 confirmed victories is unequivocal in his conclusion that the Spitfire I was superior to the Bf109E, except in the dive.

Grateful acknowledgement is made to Jeffery Quill and Alan Deere for use of their experience. The German figures are given in the adjoining table.

Me Bf109E versus British fighters

Aircraft	Engine	Max speed (mph)	Full Throttle height (feet)	Corrected BHP at FT height	Maximum speed in mph				
					SL	5,000ft	15,000ft	20,000ft	25,000ft
Bf109 (AUW 5,775 lb)	DB 601	348	17,500	950	283	302	338	343	328
Hurricane I (AUW 6,750 lb)	Merlin III	311	17,500	965	246	264	303	305	290
Hurricane II (AUW 6,800 lb)	Merlin XX	323	21,000	1,075	268	285	314	319	313
Spitfire I (AUW 6,100 lb)	Merlin III	355	18,500	965	282	302	342	351	340

Aircraft	Service Ceiling 100ft/min	Operational Ceiling (500 ft/min)	Time to operational ceiling Min Sec	Rate of climb at 30,000ft (ft/min)	Time to 30,000ft Min Sec	Rate of climb at 25,000ft (ft/min)	Time to 25,000ft Min Sec
Bf109	35,200ft	31,900ft	20 23	740	17 12	1,340	11 39
Hurricane I	35,000ft	31,400ft	21 15	660	17 30	1,260	13 12
Hurricane II	37,600ft	34,900ft	19 57	1,160	13 20	1,840	9 48
Spitfire 1	37,400ft	34,000ft	21 33	1,020	15 42	1,660	11 33

Appendix VI

The Merlin S.U. Carburettor Under Negative-G

This Appendix expands the comments made about the effects of negative-g on the S.U. carburettor on page 46 of the third edition of "The Merlin in Perspective – the combat years".

A characteristic of the Merlin which has led to some comment was the cut that occurred if negative-g was applied when entering a dive. The momentary power loss was in two stages; an initial loss of power which some pilots regarded as only a very brief hesitation, followed by a rich cut of about 1½ secs duration. Full power returned once the negative-g was removed. The tactical disadvantage it caused could be reduced by pilot technique, such as entering the dive from one wingtip. Wing Commander 'Roly' Beaumont, apart from undertaking the first flights of the Canberra bomber and Lightning fighter, flew Hurricanes in the air fighting in 1940 prior to and during the Battle of Britain, in No.87 Squadron. I am grateful to him for allowing me to use his quote at the Hurricane 50th Anniversary evening, which while dealing with the abilities of the aeroplane encompasses the engine.

"Another thing we did was to devise a manoeuvre which was aimed at getting us out of a difficult corner if ever we got into one. This may sound very extraordinary, probably, to practising pilots today, but it consisted of putting everything into the left-hand front corner of the cockpit. If you saw a 109 on your tail, and it hadn't shot you down at that point, you put on full throttle, fine pitch, full left rudder, full left stick and full forward stick. This resulted in a horrible manoeuvre, which was in fact a negative-g spiral dive. But you would come out of the bottom of it with no Me 109 on your tail and your aeroplane still intact".

Comparisons have been drawn with the direct injected DB600 series engines in the Me 109, which did not suffer in this way. The problem was known before the war, but it was thought that the British fighters would be operating as bomber destroyers and the situation would not arise, which shows how wrong one can be. The Daimler-Benz engine was good, but direct injection provided no charge cooling due to the latent heat of evaporation of fuel, which was worth 25°C reduction in charge temperature. Like all engines it had its own problems, including failures of injector pipes. Direct injection had been considered by Rolls-Royce and had been turned down in favour of the carburettor. An example of its use by the Company was the direct injected sleeve valve diesel Kestrel, powering Captain George Eyston's Flying Spray, which had for a time held long distance records and the speed record for diesel cars.

Most of the credit for reducing the negative-g problem to negligible proportions goes to the late Miss Shilling (Mrs Naylor) – Tilly to her friends, who was in charge of the carburettor section of RAE at Farnborough. This remarkable woman saw further than most through a barn door, recognising that the engine fuel pump was part of the problem. It had been designed as two separate gear pumps with individual quill drives, so if one pump were to fail the other would keep the engine running. Each pump was capable of meeting maximum engine demand plus 20%, a relief valve controlling outlet pressure. Miss Shilling saw that if the float needle was not controlling, both pumps could suddenly put a large excess of fuel into the carburettor. She developed the RAE restrictor, which was fitted in the fuel line to the carburettor and which limited the flow to just above the maximum engine demand. It seems unlikely that any were fitted during the Battle, except for a trial quantity of six. Later retrospective action was taken and was a useful palliative. The scheme finally adopted was for an anti-g version of the S.U. developed by her section, which allowed the existing carburettor to be modified. The weak cut, which was caused by the fuel in the float chambers rising to the top and starving the jets when negative-g was applied, was cured by fitting jet shrouds which continued to draw fuel from halfway up the chambers. Ball valves were added to prevent the fuel from flooding out of the air vents under this condition. The ensuing rich cut was prevented by forming a restrictor on the end of the float needle, so that when forced fully open by the fuel pressure, the floats then having lost control, the restrictor, like that fitted earlier limited the flow to slightly above maximum engine demand. This carburettor continued to be fitted to various marks of Merlin until production ceased. The changes to the S.U. carburettor to give it its anti-g characteristics are shown in the illustration.

 As mentioned in the main text a negative-g version of the S.U.carburettor was developed, in parallel with the anti-g version, to the point of undergoing service trials, but was abandoned as its mechanism could not sense zero g. On certain marks of the engine the RAE restrictor was retained, leaving the carburettor unmodified, but where the anti-g features were embodied the RAE restrictor was removed. Two-stage engines in the range of 60 to 100 series, depending upon mark number, could have either an S.U. to Bendix carburettor, the latter not being subject to g effects. The Bendix was fitted to the 65, 66, 70, 76, 77 and 85. Above 100 series single point S.U. injection was featured and again was not sensitive to g effects. Packard engines were all fitted with Bendix carburettors, with the exception of some 100 series equivalents built at the end of the war with Bendix units and Simmonds power control units.

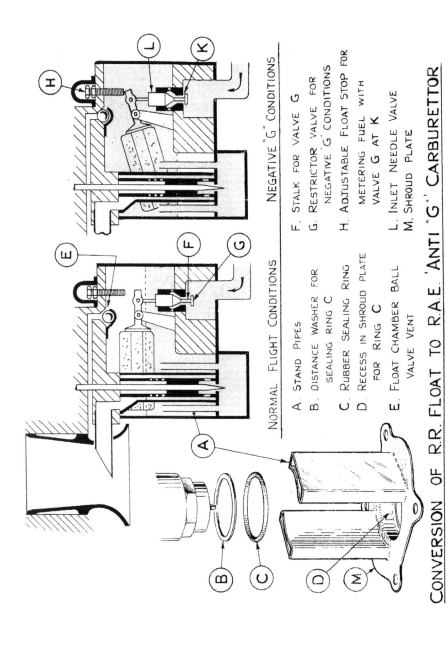

NEGATIVE "G" CONDITIONS

NORMAL FLIGHT CONDITIONS

A. STAND PIPES
B. DISTANCE WASHER FOR
   SEALING RING C
C. RUBBER SEALING RING
D. RECESS IN SHROUD PLATE
   FOR RING C
E. FLOAT CHAMBER BALL
   VALVE VENT

F. STALK FOR VALVE G
G. RESTRICTOR VALVE FOR
   NEGATIVE 'G' CONDITIONS
H. ADJUSTABLE FLOAT STOP FOR
   METERING FUEL WITH
   VALVE G AT K
L. INLET NEEDLE VALVE
M. SHROUD PLATE

CONVERSION OF R.R. FLOAT TO R.A.E. 'ANTI "G"' CARBURETTOR

Appendix VII

This section reproduces facsimilies of the listings of Mark Numbers maintained and issued by the Rolls-Royce Production Drawing Office and the Service Department by way of their Aero Service Bulletins.

They cover the single stage engines and complements similar charts for the two stage engines which were published in "THE MERLIN 100 SERIES - the ultimate military development".

ROLLS-ROYCE PISTON ENGINES
LIST OF M.O.S. MARK NUMBERS

Production Mark Number	M.O.S. Experimental Nomenclature	Supercharger Rotor Dia.	Supercharger Gear Ratios	Propeller Reduction Gear Ratio	Max. Boost P.S.I. 100/130 Grade Fuel	Max. Boost P.S.I. 115/150 Grade Fuel	Aircraft Type	Remarks
Merlin I	RM.1S	10.25	8.58	.477	+5¾	–	Battle	Glycol cooled, ramp head cylinder
Merlin II	RM.1S	10.25	8.58	.477	+12	–	Battle Hotspur Hurricane Spitfire	Glycol cooled Full diameter propeller shaft
Merlin III	RM.1S	10.25	8.58	.477	+16	–	Sea Hurricane	Glycol cooled Universal propeller shaft
Merlin III	RM.1S	10.25	8.58	.477	+12	–	Battle Henley Hotspur Hurricane Spitfire Defiant	Glycol cooled Universal propeller shaft
Merlin IV	RM.1S	10.25	8.58	.477	+?	–	Whitley	Pressure glycol cooled Necked down propeller shaft
Merlin V	RM.1S	10.25	8.58	.477	+12	–	Battle Henley Hotspur Hurricane Spitfire Defiant	Glycol cooled Necked down propeller shaft
Merlin VIII	RM.3M	10.25	6.313	.477	+9	–	Fulmar	Pressure water/glycol cooled

ROLLS-ROYCE PISTON ENGINES
LIST OF M.O.S. MARK NUMBERS

Production Mark Number	M.O.S. Experimental Nomenclature	Supercharger		Propeller Reduction Gear Ratio	Max. Boost P.S.I.		Aircraft Type	Remarks
		Rotor Dia	Gear Ratios		100/130 Grade Fuel	115/150 Grade Fuel		
Merlin X	RM.1SM	10.25	6.39/8.75	.42	+10	-	Wellington Whitley Halifax	Pressure water/glycol cooled
Merlin XII	RM.3S	10.25	9.09	.477	+12½	-	Spitfire	Pressure water/glycol cooled
Merlin XX	RM.3SM	10.25	8.15/9.49	.42	+16FS +14MS	-	Halifax Hurricane Defiant Beaufighter	Pressure water/glycol cooled Basic type replacing Merlin X
Merlin XXI	RM.3SM	10.25	8.15/9.49	.42	+16FS +14MS	-	Mosquito	As Merlin XX but reversed flow cooling
Merlin 22	RM.3SM	10.25	8.15/9.49	.42	+16FS +14MS	-	Halifax Hurricane Defiant Beaufighter	Similar to Merlin XX but two-piece cylinder blocks and improved modification standard
Merlin 22A	RM.3SM	10.25	8.15/9.49	.42	+16FS +14MS	-	Halifax Hurricane Defiant Beaufighter	Merlin XX converted to incorporate two-piece cylinder blocks
Merlin 23	RM.3SM	10.25	8.15/9.49	.42	+16FS +14MS	-	Mosquito	As Merlin 22 but with reversed flow cooling
Merlin 23A	RM.3SM	10.25	8.15/9.49	.42	+16FS +14MS	-	Mosquito	Merlin 21 converted to incorporate two-piece cylinder blocks

ISSUED BY PRODUCTION DRAWING OFFICE • ROLLS-ROYCE LIMITED DERBY   DATE ISSUED FEBRUARY 1953

Page M.2

ROLLS-ROYCE PISTON ENGINES
LIST OF M.O.S. MARK NUMBERS

Production Mark Number	M.O.S. Experimental Nomenclature	Supercharger		Propeller Reduction Gear Ratio	Max. Boost P.S.I.		Aircraft Type	Remarks
		Rotor Dia.	Gear Ratios		100/130 Grade Fuel	115/150 Grade Fuel		
Merlin 24	RM.3SM	10.25	8.15/9.49	.42	+18	–	Lancastrian	Similar to Merlin 22 but with modified boost control to permit increased ratings
Merlin T 24-1	RM.3SM	10.25	8.15/9.49	.42	+18	–	Lancastrian	Merlin 24 with improved modification standard
Merlin T 24-2	RM.3SM	10.25	8.15/9.49	.42	+18	–	Lancaster	Merlin T24-1 with improved cylinder specification
Merlin T 24-3	RM.3SM	10.25	8.15/9.49	.42	+18	–	Lancaster (Project only)	Merlin T24-2 with end to end crankshaft oil feed
Merlin 25	RM.3SM	10.25	8.15/9.49	.42	+18	–	Mosquito	Merlin 24 but with reversed flow cooling
Merlin 26	RM.3SM	10.25	8.15/9.49	.42	+18	–	Barracuda (Project only)	Merlin 24 but with Coffman starter type crankcase
Merlin 27	RM.3SM	10.25	8.15/9.49	.477	+18	–	Hurricane (Project only)	As Merlin 24 but with .477 reduction gear ratio
Merlin 28	RM.3SM	10.25	8.15/9.49	.42	+9	–	Lancaster	American built Packard version of Merlin XX but with American two-piece cylinder block

ISSUED BY PRODUCTION DRAWING OFFICE • ROLLS-ROYCE LIMITED DERBY

DATE ISSUED FEBRUARY 1953

Page M.3

ROLLS-ROYCE PISTON ENGINES
LIST OF M.O.S. MARK NUMBERS

Production Mark Number	M.O.S. Experimental Nomenclature	Supercharger Rotor Dia.	Supercharger Gear Ratios	Propeller Reduction Gear Ratio	Max. Boost P.S.I. 100/130 Grade Fuel	Max. Boost P.S.I. 115/150 Grade Fuel	Aircraft Type	Remarks
Merlin 29	RM.3SM	10.25	8.15/9.49	.477	+9	-	Hurricane	Similar to Merlin 28 but fitted with American type .477 reduction gear ratio and propeller shaft splined to suit American propellers
Merlin XXX	RM.2M	9.75	8.58	.477	+12	-	Fulmar Barracuda	Similar to Merlin VIII except for supercharger
Merlin 31	RM.3SM	10.25	8.15/9.49	.42	+9	-	Mosquito	American built Packard version of Merlin 21
Merlin 32	RM.5M	9.75	8.58	.477	+18	-	Spitfire Seafire Barracuda	Similar to Merlin 30 but with two-piece cylinder block and improved modification standard
Merlin 33	RM.3SM	10.25	8.15/9.49	.42	+9	-	Mosquito	American built Packard version of Merlin 23
Merlin 34	RM.5M	9.75	8.58	.477	+18	-		As Merlin 32 but with electric starter motor No production
Merlin T34	RM.3SM	10.25	8.15/9.49	.42	+18	-		Merlin T24-2 with gearbox drive and modified intake elbow No production
Merlin 35		9.75	8.58	.471	+12	-	Athena Balliol	Merlin T24-2 with single speed, single stage supercharger

ROLLS-ROYCE PISTON ENGINES
LIST OF M.O.S. MARK NUMBERS

| Production Mark Number | M.O.S. Experimental Nomenclature | Supercharger | | Propeller Reduction Gear Ratio | Max. Boost P.S.I. | | Aircraft Type | Remarks |
		Rotor Dia.	Gear Ratio:		100/130 Grade Fuel	115/150 Grade Fuel		
Merlin 38	RM.3SM	10.25	8.15/9.49	.42	+9	–	Lancaster	American built Merlin 22
Merlin 45	RM.5S	10.25	9.09	.477	+16	–	Spitfire	Basic type replacing Merlin III
Merlin 45M		9.5	9.09	.477	+18	–	Spitfire	Similar to Merlin 45 but with 'cropped' supercharger rotor
Merlin 46	RM.6S	10.85	9.09	.477	+16	–	Spitfire	Similar to Merlin 45 but with increased supercharger impeller diameter
Merlin 47	RM.6S	10.85	9.09	.477	+16	–	Spitfire	Similar to Merlin 46 but with modified crankcase for cabin blower drive
Merlin 50	RM.5S	10.25	9.09	.477	+16	–	Spitfire	Similar to Merlin 45 but with diaphragm controlled fuel feed in carburetter
Merlin 50A	RM.6S	10.85	9.09	.477	+16	–	Spitfire	Similar to Merlin 50 with Merlin 46 rotor and guide vanes
Merlin 50M	RM.5S	9.5	9.09	.477	+18	–	Spitfire	Similar to Merlin 50 with 'cropped' supercharger rotor
Merlin 51	RM.5S	10.25	9.09	.477	+16	–		Similar to Merlin 50 but without de-aerator
								No production

ISSUED BY PRODUCTION DRAWING OFFICE • ROLLS-ROYCE LIMITED DERBY

DATE ISSUED FEBRUARY 1953

ROLLS-ROYCE PISTON ENGINES
LIST OF COMMERCIAL MARK NUMBERS

Mark Number	Customer	Supercharger Rotor Dia.	Supercharger Gear Ratios	Propeller Reduction Gear Ratio	Max. Boost lb/sq/inch 100/130 Grade Fuel	Aircraft Type	Remarks
Merlin 500-2	B.S.A.A.	10.25	8.15/9.49	.42	+18	Lancastrian	As Merlin 500 type engines
Merlin 500-3	Alitalia Italy	10.25	8.15/9.49	.42	+18	Lancastrian	As Merlin 500 type engines
Merlin 500-4	Skyways Limited	10.25	8.15/9.49	.42	+18	Lancastrian	As Merlin 500 type engines
Merlin 500-5	Flota Aerea Mercante Argentine	10.25	8.15/9.49	.42	+18	Lancastrian	As Merlin 500 type engines
Merlin 500-6	Silver City Airways	10.25	8.15/9.49	.42	+18	Lancastrian	As Merlin 500 type engines
Merlin 500-20	Fiat	10.25	8.15/9.49	.42	+18	G.59	As Merlin 500 type engines
Merlin 500-21	Flight Refueling Limited	10.25	8.15/9.49	.42	+18	Lancastrian	As Merlin 500 type engines
Merlin 501	Trans Canadian Airways	10.25	8.15/9.49	.42	+18	Lancastrian	As Merlin T24-4 type engines
Merlin 502	-	10.25	8.15/9.49	.42	+18	-	As Merlin 500 but climbing boost increased from 9 to 12 lbs/sq.inch
Merlin 502-1	B.O.A.C.	10.25	8.15/9.49	.42	+18	Lancastrian	As Merlin 502 type engines

ISSUED BY PRODUCTION DRAWING OFFICE · ROLLS-ROYCE LIMITED DERBY

DATE ISSUED FEBRUARY 1953

MERLIN.

Single Speed - Single Stage Supercharger Series.

BASIC ENGINE FOR ALL THE FOLLOWING MARKS.

For Performance Data see Bulletin 15.

R'dn. Gear Ratio.	Supercharger. Rotor Dia.	Supercharger. Gear Ratio.	Type of Carb. or Fuel Injection Pump.	Coolant Direction of Flow.	Starter.	Remarks.		
·477	10·25″	8·58	S.U. Float type	Normal	Electric	**Prop. Shaft.** Full Dia. **Cyl. Block.** Single Piece. **Cooling.** Glycol.		

Mark No.	Aircraft.	Variations from Basic.	Mark No.	Aircraft.	Variations from Basic.
			8	Fulmar I	**Prop. Shaft.** Universal necked down type. **S C. Ratio.** 6·313. **A.B.C.** Enclosed cam type. **Cooling.** Pressure or Glycol. **Starter.** Coffman.
2	Battle I Hurricane I	—			
3	Battle I Hurricane I Spitfire I Defiant I Henley Sea Hurricane	**Prop. Shaft.** Universal necked down type.	12	Spitfire II	**Prop. Shaft.** Universal necked down type. **S·C. Ratio.** 9·09 **A.B.C.** Enclosed cam type. **Cooling.** Pressure or Glycol. **Starter.** Coffman.
4	Whitley IV	**Prop. Shaft.** First necked down type. **Cooling.** Pressure or Glycol.	30	Fulmar II Barracuda I	**Prop. Shaft.** Universal necked down type. **S C. Ratio.** 8·58 **S C. Rotor Dia.** 9·75″ **A.B.C.** Enclosed cam type. **Boost.** Take-off obtained by ·125″ dia. hole in cut out-valve. **Cooling.** Pressure or Glycol. **Starter.** Coffman.
5	Hurricane I Spitfire I Defiant I Henley Sea Hurricane	**Prop. Shaft.** Necked down type. **Cooling.** Pressure or Glycol. (Converted Merlin 3)	32	Barracuda II Seafire I, II, and III Spitfire XIII	**S·C. Ratio.** 8·58 **S·C. Rotor Dia.** 9·75″ **S·C.** Central entry type. **Carb.** R.A.E. Anti-G. **A.B.C.** Enclosed cam type. **Cyl. Block.** Two-piece. **Starter.** Coffman.

MERLIN.

Single Speed - Single Stage Supercharger Series.

BASIC ENGINE FOR ALL THE FOLLOWING MARKS.

For Performance Data see Bulletin 15.

R'dn. Gear Ratio.	Supercharger. Rotor Dia.	Supercharger. Gear Ratio.	Type of Carb. or Fuel Injection Pump.	Coolant Direction of Flow.	Starter.	Remarks.
·477	10·25″	9·09	S.U. Float Feed and R.A.E. Anti-G	Normal	Electric	**R'dn. Gear. Prop. Shaft.** Universal. **Supercharger.** Central entry. **Carburetter.** Designed as a separate unit. **Cylinder Block.** One-piece. **Cooling.** Water/Glycol pressure cooled.

Mark No.	Aircraft.	Variations from Basic.	Mark No.	Aircraft.	Variations from Basic.
45	Spitfire V Seafire I, II and III	—	50M	Spitfire V LF.	**S/C. Rotor Dia.** 9·5″ **Carb.** Diaphragm controlled fuel feed. Later deleted for R.A.E. Anti-G type.
45M	Spitfire V LF.	**S C. Rotor Dia.** 9·5″ **A.B.C.** New aneroid assembly to give − 18 lb. boost entirely by the aneroid dispensing with operation of boost control cut-off valve.	55	Seafire I, II and III	**Cyl. Block.** Two-piece.
46	Spitfire V Seafire II C	**S C. Rotor Dia.** 10·85″	55A	Spitfire V	**Cyl. Block.** Two-piece. (Modified from Merlin 50)
47	Spitfire VI	**C'Case.** Modified for cabin blower drive. **S/C. Rotor Dia.** 10·85″ **Carb.** S.U. Float type. (High altitude)	55M	Spitfire V LF. Seafire I, II and III	**S C. Rotor Dia.** 9·5″ **Cyl. Block.** Two-piece.
50	Spitfire V	**Carb.** Diaphragm controlled fuel feed. Later deleted for R.A.E. Anti-G type.	55MA	Spitfire V	**S/C Rotor Dia.** 9·5″ **Cyl. Block.** Two-piece. (Modified from Merlin 45M)
50A	Spitfire V	**S/C. Rotor Dia.** 10·85″ **Carb.** Diaphragm controlled fuel feed. Later deleted for R.A.E. Anti-G type.	56	Spitfire VI	**S/C. Rotor Dia.** 10·85″ **Cyl. Block.** Two-piece. **Carb.** Diaphragm controlled fuel feed. Later deleted for R.A.E. Anti-G type. (Modified Merlin 46)

MERLIN 35.

Single Speed - Single Stage Supercharger Series.

For Performance Data see Bulletin 15.

R'dn. Gear Ratio.	Supercharger.		Type of Carb. or Fuel Injection Pump.	Coolant Direction of Flow.	Starter.	Remarks.
	Rotor Dia.	Gear Ratio.				
0·471	9·75"	8·58	S.U. Float Feed with Temp. Control AVT. 40 233	Normal	Electric	This engine is built to the highest modification standard, see D.I.S. in T.S.D. 202. A ball type header tank with vapour separator is incorporated in the coolant system. Rocker cover breather.

Aircraft :– Athena.
Balliol.

MERLIN 10.

First Two speed - Single Stage S C. Engine.

BASIC ENGINE FOR THE FOLLOWING MARK.

R'dn. Gear Ratio.	Supercharger.		Type of Carb. or Fuel Injection Pump.	Coolant Direction of Flow.	Starter.	Remarks.
	Rotor Dia.	Gear Ratio.				
0·42	10.25"	6·39 8·75	S.U. Float Feed	Normal	Electric	**Prop. Shaft.** Universal. **Cyl. Block.** One-piece. Pressure water/glycol cooled.

Aircraft :– Whitley V.
Wellington II.
Halifax I.

MERLIN.

Two Speed – Single Stage Supercharger Series.
BASIC ENGINE FOR ALL THE FOLLOWING MARKS.
For Performance Data see Bulletin 15.

R'dn. Gear Ratio.	Supercharger.		Type of Carb. or Fuel Injection Pump.	Coolant Direction of Flow.	Starter.	Remarks.
	Rotor Dia.	Gear Ratio.				
0·42	10·25″	8·15 9·49	S.U. Float Feed and R.A.E. Anti-G	Normal	Electric	Basic type replacing Merlin 10. **Prop. Shaft.** Universal. **Cyl. Block.** One-piece. Pressure water glycol cooled. Central entry S C and carburetter as detachable unit.

Mark No.	Aircraft.	Variations from Basic.	Mark No.	Aircraft.	Variations from Basic.
20	Halifax II Hurricane II Defiant II Beaufighter II Lancaster I	—	23A	Mosquito I, II, III, IV V, VI	**Cyl. Block.** Two-piece. Reversed flow cooling. Modified in the field from Merlin 21.
21	Mosquito I, II, III, IV	Reverse flow cooling.	24	Lancastrian. Lancaster.	**Cyl. Block.** Two-piece. **Boost Control.** Modified to permit increased ratings.
22	Halifax II Lancaster I	**Cyl. Block.** Two-piece. Improved Modification standard.	T24-1	York	**Cyl. Block.** Two-piece. As Merlin 24 with improved modification standard. **Boost Control.** Modified to permit increased ratings.
22A	Halifax II Hurricane II Defiant II Beaufighter II	**Cyl. Block.** Two-piece. Modified in the field from Merlin 20.	25	Mosquito VI, XII, XIII, XVIII, XIX	**Cyl. Block.** Two-piece. Reversed flow cooling. **Note.** Certain Merlin 25 engines, special order only, have been converted to operate at + 25 lb. boost combat rating, necessitating the fitting of AVT. 40/217 carburetters.
23	Mosquito I, II, III, IV, V, VI	**Cyl. Block.** Two-piece. Reversed flow cooling.			

MERLIN TO T.24-2 MODIFICATION STANDARD.

Two Speed - Single Stage Supercharger Series.

BASIC ENGINE FOR THE FOLLOWING MARKS.

For Performance Data see Bulletin 15.

R'dn. Gear Ratio.	Supercharger.		Type of Carb. or Fuel Injection Pump.	Coolant Direction of Flow.	Starter.	Remarks.
	Rotor Dia.	Gear Ratio.				
0·42	10·25˝	8·15 9·49	S.U. Float Feed	Normal	Electric	All units strengthened or improved. Engine constructed to highest modification standard, see D.I.S. in Merlin Mods. Manual T.S.D. 202.

Mark No.	Aircraft.	Variations from Basic.	Mark No.	Aircraft.	Variations from Basic.
T24-2	Lancaster	—	25-8	Mosquito (Turkish Government)	**Coolant Direction of Flow.** Reversed.
T24	York Lancastrian. (T.C.A.)	Introduction of an after-heater.	502-1	York (B.O.A.C.)	As Merlin 500 type engines, but climbing boost increased from 9 to 12 lb. sq. in. to the special requirements of the individual operator.

MERLIN 500 SERIES.

This series is identical to the Merlin T.24-2, but termed a Merlin 500 to denote a Civil or Commercial operator, the - and number denoting the **ORIGINAL** operator. E.G. : 500-4 originally operated by Skyways Ltd.

Originally operated by :-			Aircraft.
500	–	B.O.A.C.	Lancastrian. York.
500-2	–	B.S.A.A.	Lancastrian. York.
500-3	–	Alitalia, Italy.	Lancastrian.
500-4	–	Skyways Limited.	Lancastrian. York.
500-5	–	F.A.M.A.	Lancastrian. York.
500-6	–	Silver City Airways	Lancastrian.
500-20	–	Fiat.	G.59.
500-21	–	Flight Re-Fuelling Ltd.	Lancastrian.
500-23	–	Egyptian Government.	Lancastrian.

NOTE. The Merlin 502-1 is shown above.

151

AMERICAN-BUILT MERLIN.

Two Speed – Single Stage Supercharger Series.

BASIC ENGINE FOR ALL THE FOLLOWING MARKS.

R'dn. Gear Ratio.	Supercharger.		Type of Carb. or Fuel Injection Pump.	Coolant Direction of Flow.	Starter.	Remarks.
	Rotor Dia.	Gear Ratio.				
0·42	10·25"	8·15 9·49	Bendix Stromberg injection type	Normal	Electric	**R'dn. Gear.** Universal Prop. Shaft. **Cyl. Block.** Two-piece (American). Pressure water glycol cooled.

Mark No.	Aircraft.	Variations from Basic.	Mark No.	Aircraft.	Variations from Basic.
28	Lancaster III	American-built Merlin 20. **Starter Motor Drive.** Plain gear reduction not epicyclic.	38	Lancaster III	American-built Merlin 22.
29	Hurricane (Canadian-built)	American-built Merlin 20. **R'dn. Gear Ratio.** 0·477. **Prop. Shaft.** American splined. **Dual Drive Unit.** U.S. V.1650-1 type unit. **Generator Drive.** U.S. V.1650-1 type. **Starter Motor Drive.** Plain gear reduction not epicyclic.	V.1650 –1	Kittyhawk	**R'dn. Gear Ratio.** 0·477. **Prop. Shaft.** American splines.
31	Mosquito XX	As for Merlin 28 except for :– **Coolant Direction of Flow.** Reversed.	224	Lancaster III, VII, X	American-built Merlin 24.
33	Mosquito XX	American-built Packard version of Merlin 23. **Coolant Direction of Flow.** Reversed.	225	Mosquito 25	American-built Merlin 25. **Coolant Direction of Flow.** Reversed.

Appendix VIII

This section reproduces facsimilies of the engine data compilations that were maintained by Arthur Lidsey (E/Lid) and published in the Rolls-Royce Aero Engine Data handbook.

To supplement these, two fold away charts of the main design differences of the Merlin engine are also included.

R.R. MERLIN ENGINES

Leading Common Particulars

Bore	5.4 in.
Stroke	6.0 in.
Capacity	{ 1649 cu. in. { 27.02 litres.
Compression ratio	6.0 : 1.
Direction of propeller rotation	R. H. tractor except where otherwise stated.
B.M.E.P.	$\dfrac{481 \times \text{B.H.P.}}{\text{R.P.M.}}$
Fuel	100 Octane except where otherwise stated.
(p)	Denotes projected or provisional rating only —not confirmed by type test.

Performance figures based on D.E.D.
2000 corrections.

E/Lid. April, 1948.

R.R. MERLIN ENGINES (Single Speed, Fully Supercharged).
R.M. – S. SERIES

R.R. and Air Ministry Nomenclature.	Reduction Gear Ratio.	Supercharger		Net Dry Weight lb. +2½% Tol.	Combat Power Rating. H.P./R.P.M./Altitude Rated Boost.	Take-off H.P./R.P.M. and Boost lb./sq. in.	Max. Cruising and Max. Climbing Conditions. R.P.M. Boost.	General Description.
		Gear Ratio.	Rotor Diam.					
R.M.1.S. Merlin II III IV V	.477	8.588	10.25"	1375	1310 3000 9000' 12 lb. sq. in. 1440 3000 5500' 16 lb. sq. in. (For Merlin III in Sea Hurricane only)	880 3000 6¼	Cruising 2600 +4½ Climbing 2600 +6¼	**Merlin II.**—Full diameter propeller shaft. Electric starting, glycol cooled. **Merlin III.** — Universal propeller shaft, dual accessory drive on reduction gear, electric starting, glycol cooled. **Merlin IV.**—As Merlin III but with necked-down propeller shaft and designed for pressure cooling. **Merlin V.**—As Merlin IV but glycol cooled.
R.M.2.S.	.477	8.588	10.25"	1375	1000 3000 15500' 6¼ lb. sq. in. (p)	1000 3000 +8¼	Cruising 2600 +4½ Climbing 2600 +6¼	As R.M.1.S. but with increased take-off power on 100 octane fuel. Glycol or pressure cooled. Superseded by the use of combat ratings on R.M.1.S.

R.M.3.S. **Merlin XII**	.477	9.089	10.25"	1420	1280/3000/10500' +12 lb./sq. in.	1175/3000 +12½	Cruising 2650+7 Climbing 2850+9	Basically as Merlin IV but with higher supercharger gear ratio and uses 100 octane fuel. Coffman starter, pressure water cooled. For Spitfire II.
R.M.4.S.	.477	9.089	10.25"	—	1150/3000/15750' +9 lb./sq. in. (p)	1165/3000 +12	Cruising 2650+7 Climbing 2850+9	A.V.T. 40 carburetter and improved entry elbow applied to Merlin XII. Not a production type; superseded by Merlin 45.
R.M.5.S. **Merlin 45**	.477	9.089	10.25"	1385	1515/3000/11000' +16 lb./sq. in.	1185/3000 +12	Criusing 2650+7 Climbing 2850+9	**Merlin 45.**—Basically as Merlin IV, but with higher supercharger gear ratio, A.V.T. 40 carburetter or R.A.E. anti 'g', improved entry elbow and narrow rotor. All supercharger and carburetter parts the same as Merlin XX. Electric starting, pressure water cooled, single piece blocks. **Merlin 55A.**—As Merlin 45, but with two-piece cylinder blocks.
Merlin 55A	.477	9.089	10.25"	1385				

R.R. MERLIN ENGINES (Single Speed, Fully Supercharged)—continued.

R.R. and Air Ministry Nomenclature.	Reduction Gear Ratio.	Supercharger		Net Dry Weight lb. +2½% Tol.	Combat Power Rating. H.P./R.P.M./Altitude Rated Boost.	Take-off H.P./R.P.M. and Boost lb./sq. in.	Max. Cruising and Max. Climbing Conditions. R.P.M. Boost.	General Description.
		Gear Ratio.	Rotor Diam.					
Merlin 45M	.477	9.089	9.50"	1390	1585/3000/2750' +18 lb./sq. in.	1230/3000 +12	Cruising 2650+7 Climbing 2850+9	**Merlin 45M.**—As Merlin 45, but with cropped supercharger rotor.
Merlin 55MA			10.25"					**Merlin 55MA.**—Exactly as Merlin 45M, but with two-piece cylinder blocks.
Merlin 50			10.25"	1390				**Merlin 50.**—Exactly as Merlin 45, but with diaphragm type carburetter and de-aerator. (De-aerator requires provision of pipe connections on fuel tanks.)
Merlin 51	.477	9.089	10.25"	1390	1470/3000/9250' +16 lb./sq. in.	1185/3000 +12	Cruising 2650+7	**Merlin 51.**—Exactly similar to Merlin 50 but without de-aerator. No production.
Merlin 55			10.25"	1400				**Merlin 55.**—R.A.E. anti-'g' carburetter, electric starting, pressure water cooled, two-piece cylinder blocks.
Merlin 55M			9.50"	1400	1585/3000/2750' +18 lb./sq. in.	1230/3000 +12	Climbing 2850+9	**Merlin 55M.**—As Merlin 55, but with cropped supercharger rotor.
Merlin 50M			9.50"	1390				**Merlin 50M.**—as Merlin 50, but with cropped supercharger rotor.

							Description
R.M.6.S. **Merlin 46**				1385			**Merlin 46.**—Improved altitude performance as compared with Merlin 45, achieved by larger diameter supercharger rotor, circular arc rotating guide vanes and modified diffuser. Float type carburetter or R.A.E. anti-'g'. Single piece blocks, electric starter.
Merlin 47	.477	9.089	10.85"	1400	1415/3000/14000' +16 lb./sq. in.	1100/3000 +12	Cruising 2650+7 Climbing 2850+9	**Merlin 47.**—Similar to Merlin 46 (above) except for Coffman starter type crankcase to accommodate cabin blower drive.
Merlin 50A	.477			1385				**Merlin 50A.** As Merlin 46 but with diaphragm-ve 'G' carburetter and de-aerator.
Merlin 56	.477			1385				**Merlin 56.**—As Merlin 46, but with two-piece cylinder blocks and diaphragm - ve 'G' carburetter and de-aerator. (De-aerator requires provision of pipe connections on fuel tanks.)
R.M.7.S.	.477	10.286	10.85"	—	1100/3000/26000' +9 lb./sq. in. (p)	940/3000 +9	Cruising 2650+7 Climbing 2850+9	As Merlin 47 but with intercooler integral with induction manifolds, and higher supercharger gear ratio. No production.

M.5

E/Lid.   April, 1948.

158

R.R. MERLIN ENGINES (Single Speed, Fully Supercharged)—*continued.*

R.R. and Air Ministry Nomenclature.	Reduction Gear Ratio	Supercharger		Net Dry Weight lb. +2½% Tol.	Combat Power Rating. H.P./R.P.M./Altitude Rated Boost.	Take-off H.P./R.P.M. and Boost lb./sq. in.	Max. Cruising and Max. Climbing Conditions. R.P.M. Boost.	General Description.
		Gear Ratio.	Rotor Diam.					

E/Lid.　April, 1948.

R.R. MERLIN ENGINES (Single Speed, Moderately Supercharged).

M.7

R.M. – M. SERIES.

| R.R. and Air Ministry Nomenclature. | Reduction Gear Ratio. | Supercharger | | Net Dry Weight lb. +2¼% Tol. | Combat Power Rating. H.P./R.P.M./Altitude Rated Boost. | Take-off H.P./R.P.M. and Boost lb./sq. in. | Max. Cruising and Max. Climbing Conditions. R.P.M. Boost. | General Description. |
		Gear Ratio.	Rotor Diam.					
R.M.1.M.	.477	7.32	10.25"	—	1085/3000/9750' +6 lb./sq. in. (p)	1000/3000 +6	Cruising 2600+4½ Climbing 2600+6	Similar to Merlin III, but with low ratio supercharger gear; 87 octane fuel. No production.
R.M.2.M. Merlin 30	.477	8.588	9.75"	1420	1360/3000/6000' +12 lb./sq. in.	1300/3000 +12½	Cruising 2650+7¾ Climbing 2850+9¼	100 octane M.S. rating (similar to M.S. ratio of Merlin XX). Coffman starter, pressure cooled. Single piece blocks and float type carburetter. Replacement for Merlin VIII used in the Fulmar.
R.M.3.M. Merlin VIII	.477	6.313	10.25"	1420	1275/3000/S.L. +9 lb./sq. in. or F.T.	1080/3000 +5¾	Cruising 2600+4 Climbing 2600+4	87 octane M.S. rating, for Fleet Air Arm use. Coffman starter, pressure cooling.

E/Lid. April, 1948.

160

R.R. MERLIN ENGINES (Single Speed, Moderately Supercharged)—*continued.*

R.R. and Air Ministry Nomenclature.	Reduction Gear Ratio.	Supercharger		Net Dry Weight lb. +2½% Tol.	Combat Power Rating. H.P./R.P.M./Altitude Rated Boost.	Take-off H.P./R.P.M. and Boost lb./sq. in.	Max. Cruising and Max. Climbing Conditions. R.P.M. Boost.	General Description.
		Gear Ratio.	Rotor Diam.					
R.M.4.M.	.477	6.313	10.25"	1420	1175/3000/3250' +6¾ lb./sq. in. (p)	1300/3000 +9¼	Cruising 2650+5¼ Climbing 2850+6¼	100 octane version of Merlin VIII. Specification otherwise identical. Clearance for emergency rating on Merlin VIII made this engine redundant. No production.
R.M.5.M. Merlin 32 / Merlin 34	.477	8.588	9.75"	1430	1640/3000/2000' +18 lb./sq. in.	1625/3000 +18	Cruising 2650+7 Climbing 2850+12	Merlin 32.—Replacement type for Merlin 30. Fitted with two-piece blocks, diaphragm carburetter with de-aerator, or R.A.E. anti-'g' carburetter. Approved internal modifications and boost control to permit 18 lb./sq. in. boost ratings. Increased reduction gear tooth tip clearance. Used in the Barracuda. Coffman starter. Merlin 34.—As for Merlin 32, but with electric starting. R.A.E. anti-'g' carburetter. No production.

| Merlin 35 | .4707 | 8.588 | 9.75" | 1520 | 1245/3000/11500' +9 lb./sq. in. (p) | 1280/3000 +12 | Cruising 2100+4 Climbing 2650+7 | **Merlin 35.**—Engine basically the T24-2, but fitted with the single stage supercharger and wheelcase of the Merlin 32, and a .4707:1 reduction gear. Merlin 620 cylinders and other modifications included for improved reliability for application as a power plant for Trainer aircraft such as Balliol and Athena. |

E/Lid.   April, 1948.

R.R. MERLIN ENGINES (Two Speed, Single Stage Supercharger).
R.M. – S.M. SERIES.

R.R. and Air Ministry Nomenclature.	Reduction Gear Ratio.	Supercharger		Net Dry Weight lb. +2½% Tol.	Combat Power Rating. H.P./R.P.M./Altitude Rated Boost.	Take-off H.P./R.P.M. and Boost lb./sq. in.	Max. Cruising and Max. Climbing Conditions. R.P.M. Boost.	General Description.
		Gear Ratio.	Rotor Diam.					
R.M.1.S.M. **Merlin X**	.42	6.389 8.75	10.25"	1450	1280/3000 S.L. ÷10 lb. sq. in. M.S. 1010/3000 17750' ÷5¾ lb. sq. in. F.S.	1280/3000 ÷10 or F.T.	Cruising 2600 ÷4 Climbing 2600 ÷5¾	Basically Merlin III, but with two-speed supercharger. Electric starting. Glycol or pressure water cooled.
R.M.2.S.M.	.42	8.1516 9.49	10.25"	1450	1225/3000 8750 1100/3000 15500' ÷9¾ lb. sq. in. (p)	1300/3000 ÷12½	Cruising 2650 ÷7¾ Climbing 2850 ÷9¾	Similar to Merlin X but with higher supercharger gear ratios. Superseded by Merlin XX rating. No production.
R.M.3.S.M. **Merlin XX** **Merlin 21**	.42	8.1516 9.49	10.25"	1450	1485/3000 6000' ÷14 lb. sq. in. (M.S.) 1490/3000 12500' ÷16 lb. sq. in. (F.S.)	1280/3000 ÷12	Cruising 2650 ÷7 Climbing 2850 ÷9	**Merlin XX.**—Basic type replacing Merlin X. A.V.T. 40 S.U. float carburetter, or R.A.F. anti-'g' type. Electric starting, pressure cooled, single piece cylinder blocks.

Engine							Notes
Merlin 22 22A Merlin 23 23A	.42	8.1516 9.49	10.25″	1470	1460/3000/6250′ +14 lb./sq. in. (M.S.) 1435/3000/11000′ +16 lb./sq. in. (F.S.)	1390/3000 +14	Cruising 2650+7 Climbing 2850+9	**Merlin 21.**—As for Merlin XX, but with reversed flow cooling (for Mosquito). Not installationally interchangeable with Merlin XX. **Merlin 22.**—Replacement type for Merlin XX. Two piece cylinder blocks, otherwise basically similar. **Merlin 22A.**—Exactly as Merlin 22 but designated 22A to indicate original Merlin XX built engine converted to Merlin 22 type. **Merlin 23.**—Replacement type for Merlin 21, but two-piece cylinder blocks; otherwise basically similar. Reversed flow cooling (for Mosquito). Not installationally interchangeable with Merlin 22.
Merlin 24	.42	8.1516 9.49	10.25″	1455	1635/3000/2250′ 1510/3000/9250′ +18 lb./sq. in.	1610/3000 +18	Cruising 2650+7 Climbing 2850+9	**Merlin 23A.**—Exactly as Merlin 23, but designated 23A to indicate original Merlin 21 built engines converted to Merlin 23 type. **Merlin 24.**—Similar to Merlin 22 (two-piece blocks), but with modified supercharger clutch and boost control to permit 18 lb./sq. in. boost rating. R.A.E. anti-'g' carburetter.

M.11

R.R. MERLIN ENGINES (Two Speed, Single Stage Supercharger)—continued.

R.R. and Air Ministry Nomenclature.	Reduction Gear Ratio.	Supercharger		Net Dry Weight lb. +2½% Tol.	Combat Power Rating. H.P./R.P.M./Altitude Rated Boost.	Take-off H.P./R.P.M. and Boost lb./sq. in.	Max. Cruising and Max. Climbing Conditions. R.P.M. Boost.	General Description.
		Gear Ratio.	Rotor Diam.					
Merlin 25	.42	8.1516 9.49	10.25"	1455	1635/3000/2250' 1510/3000/9250' +18 lb./sq. in.	1610/3000 +18	Cruising 2650+7 Climbing 2850+9	Merlin 25.—As for Merlin 24 above but with reversed flow coolant connections (for Mosquito). Not installationally interchangeable with Merlin 24.
Merlin 26	.477	8.1516 9.49	10.25"	1475	1635/3000/2250' 1510/3000/9250' +18 lb./sq. in.	1610/3000 +18	Cruising 2650+7 Climbing 2850+9	Merlin 26.—As Merlin 24 but with Coffman starter crankcase and .477:1 reduction gear ratio - for Barracuda. Not a production type.
Merlin 27				1455				Merlin 27.—As Merlin 24, but with altered reduction gear ratio - for Hurricane Mk. IV D.

Merlin T.24 – 1		1520	1635/3000/2250' 1510/3000/9250' + 18 lb./sq. in.	1610/3000 + 18	Cruising 2650 + 7 Climbing 2850 + 9
Merlin T.24 – 2		1540			
Merlin T.24 – 3	.42 8.1516 10.25" 9.49	1540	Max. Emergency 1595/3000/2250' 1485/3000/9250' + 18 lb./sq. in.	1570/3000 + 18	Max. Cruis'g. 1040/2650/8750 + 7 1000/2650/15500 + 7 Climbing 2850 r.p.m. + 9
Merlin T.24 – 4		1575			
Merlin T.34		—	1625/3000/2000' 1495/3000/9000' + 18 lb./sq. in. (p)	1600/3000 + 18	Max. Cruis'g. 1140/2650/6250 + 9 1115/2850/15750 + 9 Climbing 2850 + 12

M.13
Merlin T 24-1.—Basically as Merlin 24 but to a higher modification standard in order to improve reliability for Transport Command requirements.
Merlin T 24-2.—Transport purpose engine. Basically as Merlin T24-1 with further modifications, incorporating Merlin 100 type cylinder, top half crankcase, reduction gear, camshaft with parabolic cams, and coolant pump. Became basic type for Civil purposes and known as Merlin 500.
Merlin T24-3.—As Merlin T24-2 except that end-to-end crankshaft oil feed introduced. No production.
Merlin T 24-4.—Exactly as Merlin T24-2 except for introduction of after-heater for T.C.A. Lancastrian T.M.D. power plants.
Merlin T 34.—As Merlin T24-2 but with provision of 100 h.p. auxiliary gearbox drive, modified intake elbow & Merlin 620 type cylinders. Suggested for Tudor II but not proceeded with.

E/Ltd.   April, 1948.

R.R. MERLIN ENGINES (Two Speed, Single Stage Supercharger)—*continued*.

R.R. and Air Ministry Nomenclature.	Reduction Gear Ratio.	Supercharger Gear Ratio.	Supercharger Rotor Diam.	Net Dry Weight lb. $+2\frac{1}{2}\%$ Tol.	Combat Power Rating. H.P./R.P.M./Altitude Rated Boost.	Take-off H.P./R.P.M. and Boost lb./sq. in.	Max. Cruising and Max. Climbing Conditions. R.P.M. Boost.	General Description.
R.M.4.S.M.	.42	8.1516 10.5	10.25"	1520	1250/3000/12500' 1150/3000/23000' ÷ 9 lb./sq. in. (p)	1300/3000 ÷ 12	Cruising 2650 ÷ 7 Climbing 2850 + 9	Similar to Merlin XX except for increased ratio F.S. gear, and intercooler interposed between blower and induction manifolds. Intercooler pump mounted on dynamo bracket.
R.M.5.S.M.	.42	8.1516 9.49	8.55"	1430	1295/3000/2750' 1230/3000/9250' ÷ 9 lb./sq. in. (p)	1400/3000 ÷ 12	Cruising 2650 ÷ 7 Climbing 2850 + 9	Similar to Merlin XX except for reduced diameter supercharger rotor for optimum low altitude performance.
R.M.7.S.M.	.42 or .477	8.1516 10.5	10.25"	—	1250/3000/12500' 1150/3000/23000' ÷ 9 lb. sq. in. (p)	1300/3000 ÷ 12	Cruising 2650 ÷ 7 Climbing 2850 + 9	Similar to R.M.4.S.M. but increased performance obtained by the use of methanol instead of by intercooling.

M.15

E/Lid. April, 1948.

R.R. MERLIN ENGINES (Two Speed, Two Stage Supercharger, Intercooled). M.16

R.R. and Air Ministry Nomenclature.	Reduction Gear Ratio.	Supercharger Gear Ratio.	Rotor Diam.	Net Dry Weight lb. +2½% Tol.	Combat Power Rating. H.P./R.P.M./Altitude Rated Boost.	Take-off H.P./R.P.M. and Boost lb./sq. in.	Max. Cruising and Max. Climbing Conditions. R.P.M. Boost.	General Description.
R.M.6.S.M. **Merlin 60**	.42	5.52 8.41	11.5" 10.1"	1650	1280 2850/9000' 1110 2850 29000' + 9 lb./sq. in.	1390/3000 +12	Cruising 2650÷7 Climbing 2850÷9	**Merlin 60.**—Basic high altitude bomber type. Single piece cylinder blocks Coffman starter crankcase to accommodate cabin blower, electric starting, pressure cooled, A.V.T. 44 float type carburetter. Used in Wellington VI.
Merlin 62								**Merlin 62.**—Replacement engine for Merlin 60 above. Generally similar, but with two-piece cylinder blocks. Also used in Wellington VI.
R.M.8.S.M. **Merlin 61**	.42	6.39 8.03	11.5" 10.1"	1640	1565 3000/11250' 1390 3000 23500' + 15 lb. sq. in.	1280/3000 +12	Cruising 2650÷7 Climbing 2850÷12	**Merlin 61.**—Basic high altitude fighter type. Two-piece cylinder blocks. Coffman starter crankcase to accommodate cabin blower, electric starting, pressure cooled, A.V.T. 44 float type or R:A.E. anti-'g' carburetter. 15 lb./sq. in. boost maximum power rating. Used in Spitfire IX.

M.17

Merlin 63.—High altitude fighter type similar to Merlin 61, but no provision for cabin blower drive. Incorporates strengthened supercharger quill drive shaft to deal with the 18 lb./sq. in. boost maximum power rating; .477 : 1 reduction gear ratio. Used in Spitfire VIII and XI.

Merlin 63A.—As Merlin 61 basically but without provision for cabin blower; strengthened supercharger drive quill shaft.

Merlin 64.—As Merlin 63 but fitted with cabin blower drive parts as on Merlin 61. Used in Spitfire IX.

Merlin 72.—Exactly as Merlin 63 with the exception of the .42 : 1 reduction gear ratio, and reversed coolant flow. For use in Mosquito.

Merlin 73.—Exactly as Merlin 72 (above) but with cabin blower drive parts. For use in Mosquito.

Engine	Reduction gear ratio	Supercharger gear ratios	Blower dia.	Weight	Power rating		Cruising / Climbing
Merlin 63	.477	6.39 8.03	11.5″ 10.1″	1645	1710 3000/8500′ 1505 3000/21000′ +18 lb./sq. in.	1280/3000 +12	Cruising 2650+7 Climbing 2850+12
Merlin 63A				1645			
Merlin 64				1660			
Merlin 72	.42	6.39 8.03	11.5″ 10.1″	1645	1710/3000/8500′ 1505/3000/21000′ +18 lb./sq. in.	1280/3000 +12	Cruising 2650+7 Climbing 2850+12
Merlin 73				1665			

E/Lid.   April, 1948.

170

R.R. MERLIN ENGINES (Two Speed, Two Stage Supercharger, Intercooled)—continued. M.18

R.R. and Air Ministry Nomenclature.	Reduction Gear Ratio.	Supercharger - Gear Ratio.	Supercharger - Rotor Diam.	Net Dry Weight lb. +2½% Tol.	Combat Power Rating. H.P./R.P.M./Altitude Rated Boost.	Take-off H.P./R.P.M. and Boost lb./sq. in.	Max. Cruising and Max. Climbing Conditions. R.P.M. Boost.	General Description.
R.M.10.S.M. Merlin 65	.42			1645				**Merlin 65.**—Fighter engine similar to Merlin 63, but with improved low altitude performance; larger diameter first-stage supercharger rotor, with altered rotating guide vanes and diffusers. Has Bendix Stromberg injection carburetter, integral cast intercooler header tank, and strengthened supercharger drive quill shaft. Reduction gear ratio .42 : 1. For use in Mustang.
Merlin 67		5.79 7.06	12.0" 10.1"	1645	1705/3000/5750' 1580/3000/16000' +18 lb./sq. in.	1315/3000 +12	Cruising 2650+7 Climbing 2850+12	**Merlin 67.**—Exactly as Merlin 65 but with reversed flow coolant connections. For Mosquito.
Merlin 85				1665		1635/3000 +18		**Merlin 85.**—As Merlin 65 but with auxiliary gearbox drive.
Merlin 85B							Cruising	**Merlin 85B.**—As Merlin 85 but with American C.S.U. type 4.G.8 (for Australian contract).

Engine								Remarks
Merlin 86	.42	5.79 / 8.03	12.0″ 10.1″	—	1665/3000/5000′ 1440/3000/22250′ + 18 lb./sq. in.	1605/3000 + 18	MS. 2650 + 7 FS. 2850 + 7 Climbing 2850 + 12	**Merlin 86.**—Basically as Merlin 85 except for supercharger gear ratios — F.S. gear as for Merlin 76, M.S. gear as Standard Merlin 85. Specially adapted for use in high altitude Lincoln project. M.19
Merlin 66	.477	5.79 / 7.06	12.0″ 10.1″	1645	1705/3000/5750′ 1580/3000/16000′ + 18 lb./sq. in.	1315/3000 + 12	Cruising 2650 + 7 Climbing 2850 + 12	**Merlin 66.**—Exactly as Merlin 65, but with .477 reduction gear, and intercooler with separate header tank. For use in Spitfire VIII and IX. L.F.
R.M.11.S.M. Merlin 70	.477	6.39 / 8.03	12.0″ 10.1″	1645	1655/3000/10000′ 1475/3000/22250′ + 18 lb./sq. in.	1250/3000 + 12	Cruising 2650 + 7 Climbing 2850 + 12	**Merlin 70.** — Improved high altitude performance fighter engine, basically similar to Merlin 66, except for supercharger gear ratios and has the large diameter first-stage supercharger rotor with modified rotating guide vanes and diffusers, strengthened supercharger drive quill shaft and Bendix injection carburetter. No provision for cabin blower. For use in Spitfire H.F. VII and IX and XI.
Merlin 71				1665				**Merlin 71.**—Exactly as Merlin 70, but with cabin blower drive parts fitted. For use in Spitfire VII.

E/Ltd. April, 1948.

R.R. MERLIN ENGINES (Two Speed, Two Stage Supercharger, Intercooled)—*continued.* M.20

R.R. and Air Ministry Nomenclature.	Reduction Gear Ratio.	Supercharger		Net Dry Weight lb. +2½% Tol.	Combat Power Rating, H.P./R.P.M./Altitude Rated Boost.	Take-off H.P./R.P.M. and Boost lb./sq. in.	Max. Cruising and Max. Climbing Conditions. R.P.M. Boost.	General Description.
		Gear Ratio.	Rotor Diam.					
Merlin 76	.42	6.39	12.0″	1645	1655/3000/10000′ 1475/3000/22250′ +18 lb./sq. in.	1250/3000 +12	Cruising 2650+7 Climbing 2850+12	**Merlin 76.**—Similar to Merlin 70 but has .42 :1 ratio reduction gear, reversed coolant flow connections, and integral cast intercooler header tank. For use in Mosquito IX, XV, XVI, and Welkin.
Merlin 77		8.03	10.1″	1665				**Merlin 77.**—Exactly as Merlin 76 (above) but fitted with cabin blower drive parts. For use in Mosquito IX, XV, XVI, and Welkin.

M.21

E/Lid.   April, 1948.

R.R. MERLIN ENGINES (Two Speed, Two Stage Supercharger, Intercooled).

MERLIN '100' SERIES.

R.R. and Air Ministry Nomenclature.	Reduction Gear Ratio.	Supercharger		Net Dry Weight lb. $+2\frac{1}{2}\%$ Tol.	Combat Power Rating, H.P./R.P.M./Altitude Rated Boost.	Take-off H.P./R.P.M. and Boost lb./sq. in.	Max. Cruising and Max. Climbing Conditions.	General Description.
		Gear Ratio.	Rotor Diam.				R.P.M. Boost.	
R.M.14.S.M. **Merlin 100**				1680	1830/3000/5500' 1690/3000/18000' +25 lb./sq. in. (Grade 150 Fuel)	1640/3000 +18	Cruising M.S. 2650 +9 F.S. 2850 +9 Climbing 2850+12	**Merlin 100.**—New series engine similar to Merlin 85 which it replaces. Features strengthened universal crankcase for end oil feed, strengthened cylinders with rocker cover breathers, stiffened valve springs, double packless gland oil lubricated ball bearing coolant pump, improved short intake elbow for mechanical accelerator pump and petrol injection features, overhung first-stage supercharger rotor, auxiliary gearbox drive, and electric starting. For Lancaster IV and Windsor.
Merlin 101				1680				

175

E/Lid.   April, 1948.

Engine	C.R.							Description
Merlin 102	.42	5.79 7.06	12.0" 10.1"	1720	1780/3000/4500' 1650/3000/16750' +20 lb./sq. in. (p)	1725/3000 +20	Cruising M.S. 2650 +9 F.S. 2850 +9 Climbing 2850+12	M.23 **Merlin 101.**—As Merlin 100 but provision only for auxiliary gearbox drive, and reversed coolant flow connections. Replaces Merlin 67. For Mosquito N.F., B. and F.B. **Merlin 102.**—As Merlin 100 except that strengthened 60/80 H.P. auxiliary gearbox drive is fitted. Used on early Tudor I.
Merlin 102A				1720				**Merlin 102A.**—As Merlin 102 but with afterheater.
Merlin 105				—				**Merlin 105.**—As Merlin 102 but with 100 H.P. auxiliary gearbox drive fitted. No production.
Merlin 120	.375 C.R.	5.79 7.06	12.0" 10.1"	—	2080/3000/2000' 1890/3000/14750' +25 lb./sq. in. (Grade 150 Fuel) (p)	1660/3000 +18	Cruising 2650+9 M.S. 2850+12 F.S. Climbing 2850+12	**Merlin 120.**—As Merlin 100 except for .375 : 1 ratio contra rotating reduction gears, and provision for auxiliary gearbox drive. No production.
Merlin 104	.42	5.79 7.06	12.0" 10.1"	1680	1980/3000/S.L. 1830/3000/13000' +25 lb./sq. in. (150 Grade Fuel)	1640/3000 +18	Cruising 2650+9 M.S. 2850+9 F.S. Climbing 2850+12	**Merlin 104.**- As for Merlin 100 except that 76 type first stage diffuser ring fitted. Cabin blower & drive fitted and provision for auxiliary gearbox drive. Engine is actually a Merlin 114 (16 S.M.) with 14 S.M. supercharger gears and rating.

R.R. MERLIN ENGINES (Two Speed, Two Stage Supercharger, Intercooled)—*continued.*

R.R. and Air Ministry Nomenclature.	Reduction Gear Ratio.	Supercharger		Net Dry Weight lb. +2½% Tol.	Combat Power Rating, H.P./R.P.M./Altitude Rated Boost.	Take-off H.P./R.P.M. and Boost lb./sq. in.	Max. Cruising and Max. Climbing Conditions. R.P.M. Boost.	General Description.
		Gear Ratio.	Rotor Diam.					
Merlin 130	.42 RH							**Merlin 130.**—"Schneiderised" engines for De H. Hornet aircraft. As Merlin 100 (14 S.M. specification) but with strengthened "universal" crankcase with internal oil feed; down-draught intake and elbow; reversed coolant flow connections; no gearbox drive fitted. Right hand propeller rotation.—for Hornet port engine.
Merlin 131	.42 LH							**Merlin 131.**—Exactly as Merlin 130 but with left hand propeller rotation—for Hornet starboard engine.
Merlin 132	.42 RH	5.79 7.06	12.0" 10.1"	1715	1980/3000/S.L. 1830/3000/13000' +25 lb./sq. in. (150 Grade Fuel)	1640/3000 +18	Cruising 2650+9 M.S. 2850+9 F.S. Climbing 2850+12	**Merlin 132.**—As Merlin 130 but with general purpose crankcase with internal oil feed for propeller braking. R.H. propeller rotation.
Merlin 133	.42 LH							**Merlin 133.**—As Merlin 132 but with L.H. propeller rotation.
Merlin 134	.42 RH							
Merlin 135	.42 LH							

177

Merlin 134A .42 RH	5.79 7.06	12.0″ 10.1″	—	1620/3000 +18	1960/3000/S.L. 1805 3000/13000′ +25 lb. sq. in. (150 Grade Fuel)	Cruising 2650+9 Climbing 2850+12
Merlin 135A .42 LH					
Merlin 140 .512 CR	5.79 7.06	12.0″ 10.1″	1780	1640/3000 +18	1980/3000/S.L. 1830 3000/13000′ +25 lb./sq.in. (150 Grade Fuel)	Cruising 2650·9 M.S. 2850+9 F.S. Climbing 2850+12
Merlin 140S .456					
Merlin 150	See Merlin 620				

Merlin 134.—As Merlin 132 with Corlass throttle - application—Sea Hornet.

Merlin 135.—As Merlin 133 with Corlass throttle - application—Sea Hornet.

Merlin 134A.—Exactly as Merlin 134 except that modifications for low r.p.m. cruising and after heating are incorporated. R.H. propeller rotation.

Merlin 135A.—Exactly as Merlin 134A except for L.H. propeller rotation.

Merlin 140.—As Merlin 100 except for .512 ratio contra rotating reduction gears, Coffman starter, 60/80 H.P. gearbox drive and shunt cooling. For Short Sturgeon.

Merlin 140S.—Preliminary engines for Short Sturgeon. As Merlin 140 but with .456 contra rotating reduction gears.

Merlin 150.—Changed to Merlin 620.

E/Lid. April, 1948.

178

R.R. MERLIN ENGINES (Two Speed, Two Stage Supercharger, Intercooled)—*continued.* M.26

R.R. and Air Ministry Nomenclature.	Reduction Gear Ratio.	Supercharger		Net Dry Weight lb. +2½% Tol.	Combat Power Rating. H.P./R.P.M./Altitude Rated Boost.	Take-off H.P./R.P.M. and Boost lb./sq. in.	Max. Cruising and Max. Climbing Conditions. R.P.M. Boost.	General Description.
		Gear Ratio.	Rotor Diam.					
R.M.16.S.M. Merlin 110	.471							The Merlin 16 S.M. series is basically the same specification as the 14 S.M. series. The main difference is in the supercharger gear ratios.
Merlin 112								**Merlin 110.**—As for Merlin 102 except for supercharger gear ratios and reduction gear ratio. Provision for fitting auxiliary gearbox drive. To replace Merlin 70 in P.R. Spitfire.
Merlin 113	.42	6.39 8.03	12.0″ 10.1″	1680	1690/3000/13000′ 1345/3000/27250′ +18 lb./sq. in.	1225/3000 +18	Cruising 2650+7 M.S. 2850+7 F.S. Climbing 2850+12	**Merlin 112.**—As Merlin 110 but with provision for cabin blower. To replace Merlin 71 in P.R. Spitfire.
Merlin 113A								**Merlin 113.**—As Merlin 110 but with .42 reduction gear and reversed flow coolant connections for replacing Merlin 76 in P.R. Mosquito.
Merlin 114								
Merlin 114A								

179

M.27

Merlin 113A.—As Merlin 113 but with Merlin 76 anti-surge supercharger diffuser fitted.

Merlin 114.—As Merlin 113 except that cabin blower fitted.

Merlin 114A.—As Merlin 114 except that Merlin 76 type anti-surge supercharger diffusers fitted.

E/Lid.   April, 1948.

R.R. MERLIN ENGINES – CIVIL TYPE – 500 SERIES
(Single Stage, Two Speed Supercharger).

R.R. and Civil Nomenclature.	Reduction Gear Ratio.	Supercharger Gear Ratio.	Rotor Dam.	Net Dry Weight lb. +2½% Tol.	Emergency Max. Power Rating H.P./R.P.M./Altitude Rated Boost. lb./sq. in.	Max. Cruising H.P./R.P.M. Altitude Rated Boost lb./sq. in.	Take-off and Climb H.P./R.P.M. Boost lb./sq. in.	General Description.
Merlin 500	.42	8.15 9.49	10.25"	1520	1635 3000 2250' 1510 3000 9250' 18 lb. sq. in.	1080 2650 /8750' 1015 2650 /15500' 7	Take-off 1610 3000 18 Climbing 1120 2850 9 M.S. 995 2850 9 F.S.	Merlin 500 series engines are single stage, two speed supercharger type, basically to R.M. 3 S.M. specification, and are adaptations of the Transport Command Series T24-2 and T24-4 engines for Civil Installations.
Merlin 500-2								Merlin 500.—Variant of T24-2 engine as used by B.O.A.C.
Merlin 500-3								Merlin 500-2.—As Merlin 500 with special features for B.S.A.A.
Merlin 500-4								Merlin 500-3.—As Merlin 500 with special features for B.E.A.
Merlin 500-5								Merlin 500-4.—As Merlin 500 with special features for Skyways Ltd.
Merlin 500-6								Merlin 500-5.—As Merlin 500 with special features for F.A.M.A. (Argentina)

| Merlin 501 | .42 | 8.15 9.49 | 10.25" | 1575 | 1595/3000/2250' 1485/3000/9250' +18 lb. sq. in. | 1040/2650 /8750' 1000/2650 /15500' +7 | Take-off 1570/3000 +18 Climbing 1085/2850 +9 M.S. 985/2850 +9 F.S. | Merlin 500-6.—As Merlin 500 with special features for Silver City Airways. Merlin 501.—Civil version of the Merlin T24-4 incorporating a charge after-heater. Otherwise as Merlin 500. Merlin 502.—As Merlin 500 but with climbing boost uprated from 9 lb./sq. in. to 12 lb./sq. in. |
| Merlin 502 | .42 | 8.15 9.49 | 10.25" | 1575 | 1635/3000/2250' 1510/3000/9250' +18 lb./sq. in. (p) | 1150/2650 /6250' 1090/2650 /13250' +9 | Take-off 1610/3000 +18 Climbing 1280/2850 +12 | |

R.R. MERLIN ENGINES – CIVIL TYPE – 600 SERIES
(Two Stage, Two Speed Supercharger).

R.R. and Civil Nomenclature.	Reduction Gear Ratio.	Supercharger		Net Dry Weight lb. +2½% Tol.	Emergency Max. Power Rating H.P./R.P.M./Altitude Rated Boost. lb./sq. in.	Max. Cruising H.P./R.P.M. Altitude Rated Boost lb./sq. in.	Take-off and Climb H.P./R.P.M. Boost lb./sq. in.	General Description.
		Gear Ratio.	Rotor Diam.					
Merlin 600 Series.								Merlin 600 series engines are basically R.M.14S.M. type, but incorporate charge heating.
Merlin 600	.42							Merlin 600.—Exactly as Merlin 102A and used on B.O.A.C. Tudor I. 60/80 H.P. gearbox fitted.
Merlin 601								Merlin 601.—As Merlin 600 except that 100 H.P. auxiliary gearbox fitted.
Merlin 604								Merlin 604.—As Merlin 600 but with Merlin 76 type first stage diffuser ring; cabin blower fitted. Supplied to Argentine Govt. for prototype "Calquin" A/C.
Merlin 620 Series.								
Merlin 620	.471							Merlin 620.—Basically as Merlin 102 'cleaned up'. General purpose non-Coffmann type crankcase with

183

Merlin 621

Merlin 621-2 } .42

Merlin 621-5

5.79 12.0" 1740 1780/3000/4500' 1180/2650
7.06 10.1"   (59°C)   /10500'
                   1655/3000/16750' 1165/2850
                   (63.5°C)   /23750'
                   +20 lb./sq. in.   +9

Take-off
1725/3000
+20
Climbing
1300/2350
+12 M.S.
1135/2850
+12 F.S.

M.31
internal oil feed to both ends of crankshaft; internal oil feed to cylinder head and rocker mechanism; internal crankcase breather passages; provision rocker cover slinging; standardisation of "thin" cylinder head; increased thickness chromium plating on rocker pads; charge afterheater; Merlin 76 type anti-surge diffusers; .471 ratio reduction gear; propeller with American splines; 100 h.p. auxiliary gearbox. For T.C.A. D.C.4M aircraft.

Merlin 621.—Exactly as Merlin 620 but with .42 reduction gear and English splined propeller shaft. For B.O.A.C. Tudor II.

Merlin 621-2.—As Merlin 621 with special features for B.S.A.A. Tudor IV and V.

Merlin 621-5.—As Merlin 621 with special features for F.A.M.A. Tudor VI.

R.R. MERLIN ENGINES – CIVIL TYPE – 620 SERIES
(Single Stage, Two Speed Supercharger)—*continued.*

R.R. and Civil Nomenclature.	Reduction Gear Ratio.	Supercharger Gear Ratio.	Supercharger Rotor Diam.	Net Dry Weight lb. +2¼% Tol.	Emergency Max. Power Rating H.P./R.P.M./Altitude Rated Boost lb./sq. in.	Max. Cruising H.P./R.P.M. Altitude Rated Boost lb./sq. in.	Take-off and Climb H.P./R.P.M. Boost lb./sq. in.	General Description.
Merlin 622	.471	5.79	12.0"	1740			Take-off 1760/3000 +20½ Climbing 1480/2850 (7500')+14 1405/2850 (18000')+14 20½ lb./sq. in.	**Merlin 622.**–As Merlin 620 with climbing boost increased from 12 to 14 lb./sq. in. & take-off boost increased from 20 to 20½ lb./sq. in.
Merlin 623	.42				1810/3000/3750' (M.S.) +20½ lb./sq. in. (p)	1175/2650 /10250'. 1170/2850 /23250'. +9		**Merlin 623.**–As Merlin 621 with climbing boost increased from 12 to 14 lb./sq. in. and take-off boost increased from 20 to 20½ lb./sq. in.
Merlin 624	.42						Take-off 1770/3000 +20	**Merlin 624.**–As Merlin 622 but with .42 in place of 4.71 reduction gear.
Merlin 630	.471	7.06	10.1"				Climbing 1465/2850 (9750')+12 1380/2850 (20000')+12	**Merlin 630.**–As Merlin 620 but with 7:1 compression ratio. Boost ratings as Merlin 620.
Merlin 631	.42				1820/3000/4000' (M.S.) +20 lb./sq. in. (p)	1225/2650 /10250'. 1210/2850 /23250'. +9		**Merlin 631.**–As Merlin 621 but with 7:1 compression ratio. Boost ratings as Merlin 621.

| Merlin 640 | .471 | 1740/3000/5000' (M.S.) +19 lb./sq. in. (p) | 1190/2650 /10250'. 1170/2850 /23250'. +9 | Take-off 1675/3000 +19 Climbing 1425/2850 (9500') +12 1340/2850 (20000') +12 | M.33 Merlin 640.—As Merlin 620 but with 6.3:1 compression ratio. Take-off boost reduced to 19 lb./ sq. in. Merlin 640.—As Merlin 621 but with 6:3.1 compression ratio. Take-off boost reduced to 19 lb./ sq. in. |
| Merlin 641 | .42 | | | | |

E/Ltd. April, 1948.

M.34

R.R. and Civil Nomenclature.	Reduction Gear Ratio.	Supercharger		Net Dry Weight lb. +2½% Tol.	Emergency Max. Power Rating H.P./R.P.M./Altitude Rated Boost. lb/sq. iu...	Max. Cruising H.P./R.P.M. Altitude Rated Boost lb./sq.in.	Take-off and Climb H.P./R.P.M. Boost lb./sq.in.	General Description.
		Gear Ratio.	Rotor Diam.					

E/Lid.   April, 1948.

PACKARD MERLIN ENGINES—BRITISH INSTALLATIONS [1]

Nomenclature and Application.	Reduction Gear Ratio.	Supercharger. Gear Ratios.	Supercharger. Rotor Diams.	Net Dry Weight lbs.	Performance Data.	General Description.
Merlin 28. British-produced Lancaster III and Canadian Lancaster X.	.422	8.15 9.49	10.25″	1475	**Combat.** 1240/3000/11500′ } +9 lbs. 1120/3000/18500′ } boost. **Take-off.** 1300/3000+12 lbs. boost. **Cruise.** 2650 r.p.m. +7 lbs. boost. **Climb.** 2850 r.p.m. +9 lbs. boost.	Packard version of Merlin XX. American type two-piece cylinder blocks. Bendix PD-16B1 carburetter. Eclipse starter with spur reduction gears. British splined propeller shaft and British accessories.
Merlin 29. Canadian-built Hurricane.	.477	8.15 9.49	10.25″	1475	Same as **Merlin 28.**	Similar to Merlin 28, but with parts taken from V-1650-1 for American splined propeller shaft and American accessories.
Merlin 31. Canadian-built Mosquito.	.422	8.15 9.49	10.25″	1475	Same as **Merlin 28 and 29.**	Packard-built Merlin 21. Similar to Merlin 28, but with reverse flow coolant connections.

PACKARD MERLIN ENGINES—BRITISH INSTALLATIONS (*continued*)

Nomenclature and Application.	Reduction Gear Ratio.	Supercharger. Gear Ratios.	Rotor Diams.	Net Dry Weight lbs.	Performance Data.	General Description.
Merlin 33. Canadian- and Australian-built Mosquito.	.422	8.15 9.49	10.25″	1500	**Combat.** 1240/3000/11500′ ⎱ +9 lbs. 1120/3000/18500′ ⎰ boost. **Take-off.** 1400/3000 +14 lbs. boost. **Cruise.** 2650 r.p.m. +7 lbs. boost. **Climb.** 2850 r.p.m. +9 lbs. boost.	Packard-built Merlin 23. British type two-piece cylinder blocks, reverse flow coolant connections. Same as Merlin 38, except for the reversed flow coolant connections.

189

PACKARD MERLIN ENGINES—BRITISH INSTALLATIONS *(continued)*

| Nomenclature and Application. | Reduction Gear Ratio. | Supercharger. | | Net Dry Weight lbs. | Performance Data. | General Description. |
		Gear Ratios.	Rotor Diams.			
Merlin 38. British-built Lancaster III. Canadian-built Lancaster X.	.422	8.15 9.49	10.25″	1500	Same as **Merlin 33.**	Packard version of Merlin 22. Same as Merlin 28, except British type two-piece cylinder blocks fitted, strengthened connecting rods (Mod. 399) and ball bearing coolant pump. Bendix PD.16.B1 carburetter.
Merlin T38. T.C.A. Lancaster.						**T.38.** Standard Merlin 38 brought up to latest Mod. standard by fitting British blended radius connecting rods, cylinder blocks and parts for 18 lbs. boost; also S.U. carburetter complete with supercharger.

PACKARD MERLIN ENGINES—BRITISH INSTALLATIONS (*continued*)

Nomenclature and Application.	Reduction Gear Ratio.	Supercharger.		Net Dry Weight lbs.	Performance Data.	General Description.
		Gear Ratios.	Rotor Diams.			
Merlin 68. Lincoln II. British- and Canadian-built. **Merlin 69.** Canadian- and Australian-built Mosquito.	.422	5.80 7.35	10.1″ 12.0″	1675	**Combat.** 1710/3000/6400′ 1490/3000/19400′ } +18 lbs. boost. **Take-off.** 1670/3000 +18 lbs. boost. **Cruise.** 2650 r.p.m. +7 lbs. boost. **Climb.** 2850 r.p.m. +12 lbs. boost.	**Merlin 68.** Packard version of Merlin 85. Same as V-1650-7, except for auxiliary gear box drive, deletion of vacuum pump and hydraulic pump drives, Merlin 61 type generator mounting, altered blower gear ratios, Bendix PD.18.B1 or PD.18.D1A carburetter, epicyclic blower gears and plain bearings for impeller shaft; two-stage inter-cooled engine. **Merlin 69.** Same as Merlin 68, except for reverse flow coolant connections and no provision for auxiliary gearbox drive.

E/Lid. May, 1945

PACKARD MERLIN ENGINES—BRITISH INSTALLATIONS (*continued*)

Nomenclature and Application.	Reduction Gear Ratio.	Supercharger. Gear Ratios.	Supercharger. Rotor Diams.	Net Dry Weight lbs.	Performance Data.	General Description.
Merlin 224. British Lancaster III. Canadian Lancaster X. **Merlin 225.** Canadian- and Australian-built Mosquito.	.422	8.15 9.49	10.25″	1500	**Combat.** 1680/3000/2500′ } +18 lbs. 1545/3000/9800′ } boost. **Take-off.** 1635/3000 +18 lbs. boost. **Cruise.** 2650 r.p.m. +7 lbs. boost. **Climb.** 2850 r.p.m. +9 lbs. boost.	**Merlin 224.** Packard version of Merlin 24. Same as Merlin 38, except for double girder pistons, strengthened supercharger drive, 4G8 C.S. unit, strengthened spring drive shaft, heavier clutch weights and strengthened M.S. clutch, stiffened crankcase panels and 25 deg. pressure angle reduction gears. **Merlin 225.** Packard version of Merlin 25. Same as Merlin 224, except for reverse flow coolant connections and scavenge outlet bracket drilled for Teleflex cutout control.

PACKARD MERLIN ENGINES—BRITISH INSTALLATIONS (continued)

Nomenclature and Application.	Reduction Gear Ratio.	Supercharger.		Net Dry Weight lbs.	Performance Data.	General Description.
		Gear Ratios.	Rotor Diams.			
Merlin 266-P. Spitfire 16LF.	.479	5.30 7.35	10.1" 12.0"	1675	**Combat.** 1710/3000/6400' ⎱ +18 lbs. 1490/3000/19400' ⎰ boost. **Take-off.** 1670/3000 +18 lbs. boost. **Cruise.** 2650 r.p.m. +7 lbs. boost. **Climb.** 2850 r.p.m. +12 lbs. boost.	Merlin 66 type engine. Same as Merlin 69, except for Rotol propeller oil pipes, 12-volt starter, solenoid for supercharger change, no fire extinguishing pipes, modified Bendix PD.18.Bl carburetter with spring return cut-out and Merlin 66 type dual drive. Normal type coolant flow.

PACKARD MERLIN ENGINES—BRITISH INSTALLATIONS (continued)

Nomenclature and Application.	Reduction Gear Ratio.	Supercharger. Gear Ratios.	Supercharger. Rotor Diams.	Net Dry Weight lbs.	Performance Data.	General Description.
Merlin 300. British- and Canadian-built Lincoln. **Merlin 301.** Canadian- and Australian-built Lincoln.	.42	5.80 7.35	10.1″ 12.0″	1675	**Combat.** 2075/3000/1900′ } +25 lbs. 1890/3000/14750′ } boost. **Take-off.** 1660/3000 +18 lbs. boost. **Cruise.** 2650 r.p.m. +9 lbs. boost. **Climb.** 2850 r.p.m. +12 lbs. boost.	**Merlin 300.** Packard version of Merlin 100, with Bendix speed density injection pump type SD.400C1, without water alcohol injection. Same as V-1650-11, except for auxiliary gearbox drive, deletion of vacuum pump drive and undercarriage pump drive, modified version of British Merlin XX type boost control, Merlin 100 breathers, no electric primer and altered supercharger drive ratios. **Merlin 301.** Same as Merlin 300 except for reverse flow coolant connections, no auxiliary gearbox drive and provision of undercarriage and vacuum pump drives.

E. Ltd. May, 1945

PACKARD MERLIN ENGINES—BRITISH INSTALLATIONS *(continued)*

Nomenclature and Application.	Reduction Gear Ratio.	Supercharger.		Net Dry Weight lbs.	Performance Data.	General Description.
		Gear Ratios.	Rotor Diams.			

E/Lid.   May. 1945

PACKARD MERLIN ENGINES—AMERICAN INSTALLATIONS [9]

Nomenclature and Application.	Reduction Gear Ratio.	Supercharger.		Net Dry Weight lbs.	Performance Data.	General Description.
		Gear Ratios.	Rotor Diams.			
V-1650-1. Kittyhawk II.	.477	8.15 9.49	10.25″	1510	**Combat.** 1240/3000/11500′ 1120/3000/18500′ } +9 lbs. boost. **Take-off.** 1300/3000 +12 lbs. boost. **Cruise.** 2650 r.p.m. +7 lbs. boost.	Packard version of Merlin XX, except for American splined propeller shaft, American generator bracket and generator drive coupling; dual drive assembly to suit American accessories and Cuno oil filter. Bendix carburetter type PD.16.A1.

PACKARD MERLIN ENGINES—AMERICAN INSTALLATIONS (*continued*)

Nomenclature and Application.	Reduction Gear Ratio.	Supercharger. Gear Ratios.	Supercharger. Rotor Diams.	Net Dry Weight lbs.	Performance Data.	General Description.
V-1650-3. Mustang P.51B and P.51C.	.479	6.39 8.095	10.1" 12"	1700	**Combat.** 1600/3000/11800′ +18¼ lbs. 1330/3000/23300′ boost. **Take off.** 1380/3000+15¼ lbs. boost. **Cruise.** 2700 r.p.m. +8 lbs. boost.	Packard version of Merlin 61. Two-piece blocks as Merlin 38, two-speed two-stage supercharger with intercooler; plain bearings for impeller shaft; epicyclic blower gears; solenoid controlled hydraulic supercharger clutches. Bendix PD.18.A1 or PD.18.C1A carburetter. U.S. No. 50 propeller shaft. Dual drive to suit American accessories, American fuel pump and generator, Bendix starter. Increased diameter spring drive shaft. Boost control modified for 18 lbs. boost. Ball bearing coolant pump.

PACKARD MERLIN ENGINES—AMERICAN INSTALLATIONS (*continued*)

Nomenclature and Application.	Reduction Gear Ratio.	Supercharger.		Net Dry Weight lbs.	Performance Data.	General Description.
		Gear Ratios.	Rotor Diams.			
V-1650-5. Kingcobra.	—	6.39 8.095	10.1" 12.0"	1575	Same as **V-1650-3.**	Same as V-1650-3, except for absence of reduction gear and propeller shaft. Special adapter flange for driving remotely mounted propeller. U.S.A. ball bearing coolant pump. Blended radius connecting rods. Never in production.
V-1650-7. Mustang P.51D.	.479	5.80 7.35	10.1" 12.0"	1715	**Combat.** $\left.\begin{array}{l}1720/3000/6200' \\ 1505/3000/19300'\end{array}\right\}$ $\left.\begin{array}{l}+18\frac{1}{4}\text{ lbs.} \\ \text{boost.}\end{array}\right\}$ **Take-off.** $1490/3000 + 15\frac{1}{4}$ lbs. boost. **Cruise.** 2700 r.p.m. $+8$ lbs. boost.	Same as V-1650-3, except for altered supercharger drive gear ratios. Now has blended radius connecting rods.

Lid. May. 1945

PACKARD MERLIN ENGINES—AMERICAN INSTALLATIONS (*continued*)

Nomenclature and Application.	Reduc- tion Gear Ratio.	Supercharger. Gear Ratios.	Rotor Diams.	Net Dry Weight lbs.	Performance Data.	General Description.
V-1650-9. Mustang P.51H. **V-1650-9A.** Mustang P.51D.	.479	6.39 8.095	10.1″ 12.0″	1725	**Combat.** 1930/3000/10100′ ⎫ +25 lbs. 1630/3000/23500′ ⎭ boost. **Take-off.** 1830/3000 +25 lbs. boost. **Cruise.** 2700 r.p.m. +8 lbs. boost.	**V-1650-9.** Packard version of Merlin 100, but fitted with Bendix PD.18.C3A injection carburetter with electric primer and water alcohol injection. Strengthened main castings and end to end crankshaft oil feed. Merlin 100 type valve fittings, sealed ball bearing coolant pump. Simmonds boost control with provision for interconnected air-screw control. Vacuum pump drive in normal position, but no C.S. unit drive. Coolant outlets at front, but pointing backwards and incorporating filler cap. U.S. No. 5 propeller shaft. External installation features to suit N.A.A. P.51H aircraft. **V-1650-9A.** Same as V-1650-9, but external installation features same as V-1650-7 to suit existing N.A.A. P.51D aircraft.

PACKARD MERLIN ENGINES—AMERICAN INSTALLATIONS (*continued*)

Nomenclature and Application.	Reduction Gear Ratio.	Supercharger.		Net Dry Weight lbs.	Performance Data.	General Description.
		Gear Ratios.	Rotor Diams.			
V-1650-11. Mustang P.51H. N.A.A.-XP.82.	.479	6.39 8.095	10.1" 12.0"	1715	Same as **V-1650-9.**	Same as V-1650-9, but with Bendix speed density carburetter type SD.400.C2, using water injection; also with vacuum pump drive taken off auxiliary gearbox drive, using Merlin 300 parts.
V-1650-13. Mustang.	.479	6.39 8.095	10.1" 12.0"	1700	Same as **V-1650-3.**	Same as V-1650-3, except for blended radius connecting rods and Simmonds SA.5 boost control without C.S.U. interconnection. This engine was never built and is now obsolete.
V-1650-15. Kingcobra.	—	6.39 8.095	10.1" 12.0"	1575	Same as **V-1650-3.**	Same as V-1650-5, except Simmonds SA.5 boost control fitted. This engine was never built and is now obsolete.

E/Lid. May, 1945

PACKARD MERLIN ENGINES—AMERICAN INSTALLATIONS (*continued*)

Nomenclature and Application.	Reduction Gear Ratio.	Supercharger. Gear Ratios.	Supercharger. Rotor Diams.	Net Dry Weight lbs.	Performance Data.	General Description.
V-1650-17. Mustang P.51D.	.479	5.80 7.35	10.1" 12.0"	1715	Same as **V-1650-7.**	Same as V-1650-7, except Simmonds SA.5 boost control fitted without C.S.U. interconnection. Only two engines built; type now obsolete.
V-1650-19. Not yet allocated to an aircraft.	.479	Variable from 5.0 to 8.3	10.1" 12.0"	1770	**Combat.** 2200/3000/S.L. 1875/3000/17000' 680/3000/42000' **Take-off.** 1700/3000 + 19¾ lbs. boost. **Cruise.** 2700 r.p.m. + 8 lbs. boost.	Same as V-1650-11, but with Sundstrand infinitely variable supercharger drive.

E Lid.   May, 1945.

PACKARD MERLIN ENGINES—AMERICAN INSTALLATIONS (*continued*)

Nomenclature and Application.	Reduction Gear Ratio.	Supercharger.		Net Dry Weight lbs.	Performance Data.	General Description.
		Gear Ratios.	Rotor Diams.			
V-1650-21. N.A.A.-XP.82.	.479	6.39 8.095	10.1" 12.0"	1750	Same as **V-1650-9.**	Same as V-1650-11, but with reversed rotation propeller shaft for twin-engined North American Aviation Corporation Exptl. fighter.
V-1650-23. N.A.A.-XP.82.	.479	6.39 8.095	10.1" 12.0"	1725	Same as **V-1650-9.**	As V-1650-11, but with V-1650-9 type PD.18.C3A injection carburetter and elbow.
V-1650-25. N.A.A.-XP.82.	.479	6.39 8.095	10.1" 12.0"	1760	Same as **V-1650-9.**	Reversed propeller rotation engine, as V-1650-21, but with V-1650-9 type PD.18.C3A injection carburetter and elbow.

15

E/Lid.   May, 1945

PACKARD MERLIN ENGINES—AMERICAN INSTALLATIONS (*continued*)

Nomenclature and Application.	Reduction Gear Ratio.	Supercharger.		Net Dry Weight lbs.	Performance Data.	General Description.
		Gear Ratios.	Rotor Diams.			

The Historical Series is published as a joint initiative by the Rolls-Royce Heritage Trust and The
Rolls-Royce Enthusiasts' Club.

Also published in the series:

No 24	*The Rolls-Royce Tyne*
	L Haworth, RRHT 1998
No 25	*A View of Ansty*
	D E Williams, RRHT 1998
No 26	*Fedden – the life of Sir Roy Fedden*
	Bill Gunston OBE FRAeS, RRHT 1998
No 27	*Lord Northcliffe – and the early years of Rolls-Royce*
	Hugh Driver, RREC 1998
No 28	*Boxkite to Jet – the remarkable career of Frank B Halford*
	Douglas R Taylor, RRHT 1999
No 29	*Rolls-Royce on the front line – the life and times of a Service Engineer*
	Tony Henniker, RRHT 2000
No 30	*The Rolls-Royce Tay engine and the BAC One-Eleven*
	Ken Goddard, RRHT 2001
No 31	*An account of partnership – industry, government and the aero engine*
	G P Bulman, RRHT 2002
No 32	*The bombing of Rolls-Royce at Derby in two World Wars – with diversions*
	Kirk, Felix and Bartnik, RRHT 2002
Special	*Sectioned drawings of piston aero engines*
	L Jones, RRHT 1995
Monograph	*Rolls-Royce Armaments*
	D Birch, RRHT 2000

The Technical Series is published by the Rolls-Royce Heritage Trust.

Also published in the series:

No 1	*Rolls-Royce and the Rateau Patents*
	H Pearson, RRHT 1989
No 2	*The vital spark! The development of aero engine sparking plugs*
	K Gough, RRHT 1991
No 3	*The performance of a supercharged aero engine*
	S Hooker, H Reed and A Yarker, RRHT 1997
No 4	*Flow matching of the stages of axial compressors*
	Geoffrey Wilde OBE, RRHT 1999
No 5	*Fast jets – the history of reheat development at Derby*
	Cyril Elliott, RRHT 2001
No 6	*Royce and the vibration damper*
	T C Clarke, RRHT 2003

Books are available from:
Rolls-Royce Heritage Trust, Rolls-Royce plc, Moor Lane, PO Box 31, Derby DE24 8BJ